5
YEAR

Class

Fiction and Poetry Texts

Eileen Jones

Published in 2004 by:
Nelson Thornes Ltd
Delta Place
27 Bath Road
CHELTENHAM
GL53 7TH
United Kingdom

04 05 06 07 08 / 10 9 8 7 6 5 4 3 2 1

A catalogue record for this book is available from the British Library

ISBN 0-7487-8649-X

Illustrations by Martha Hardy, Kate Sheppard, Lisa Williams
Page make-up by GreenGate Publishing Services

Printed in Great Britain by Ashford Colour Press

Acknowledgements

All texts written by and copyright Eileen Jones except:

Matilda Copyright © Roald Dahl by kind permission of Jonathan Cape Ltd and
Penguin Books Ltd. Illustration by Quentin Blake from *Matilda* by Roald Dahl
published by Jonathan Cape. Used by permission of The Random House Group
Limited; *The Peppermint Pig* Curtis Brown on behalf of Nina Bawden. Copyright ©
Nina Bawden (1975); *Harry Potter and the Philosopher's Stone* Copyright © J. K.
Rowling 1998; *Charlie and the Chocolate Factory: A Play* Copyright © Roald Dahl
& Richard R George, published by Penguin; *Problems* by Jacqueline Wilson (first
published in the BBC Children In Need Story Collection) Copyright © Jacqueline
Wilson 2002; *Carrie's War* Copyright © Nina Bawden 1973; 'A Day in the Life of
Danny the Cat' from *Talking Turkeys* Copyright © Benjamin Zephaniah 1994
(Viking 1994); 'Days' Copyright © Brian Moses; 'Little Red Riding Hood and the
Wolf' Copyright © Roald Dahl, *Revolting Rhymes* published by Jonathan Cape Ltd
and Penguin Books; *The Blue Fish* Copyright © Pie Corbett first published in
Junior Education; 'The Listeners' Copyright © The Literary Trustees of Walter de la
Mare and the Society of Authors as their representative; *How Fire Came to Earth*
Copyright © Lucy Coats, *Atticus the Storyteller's Greek Myths* published by Orion
Children's Books; *Out of the Shadows* Copyright © Jamila Gavin published by
Egmont; *The Jungle Book* A.P Watt Ltd on behalf of the National Trust for Places
of Historical Interest or Natural Beauty; extract from *Tom's Midnight Garden* by
Philippa Pearce, Copyright © Oxford University Press 1958, reprinted by
permission of Oxford University Press

Cover image: 10109573 Opening Ceremony © Peter Tarry/Action Plus

Every effort has been made to trace the copyright holders, but if any have been
inadvertently overlooked, the publishers will be pleased to make the necessary
arrangement at the first opportunity.

Contents

How to use this book

What this book contains	• Extracts from published works, plus tailor-made extracts, all arranged and chosen specifically to match the examples of medium-term planning provided by the National Literacy Strategy
	• Teaching ideas for each extract to get you started, covering some of the relevant text, sentence or word level objectives from the relevant unit
How you can use *Classworks Literacy Texts* with other resources	• The blocked unit structure means you can dip into the book to find resources perfect for what you're teaching this week – it doesn't matter what plan, scheme or other resource you're using
	• There are two *Classworks Literacy Texts* books for every year from Reception (or Primary 1) to Year 6 (or Primary 7): one contains Fiction and Poetry, the other contains Non-fiction. Both books together contain texts for every unit of the medium-term plans

What each page does

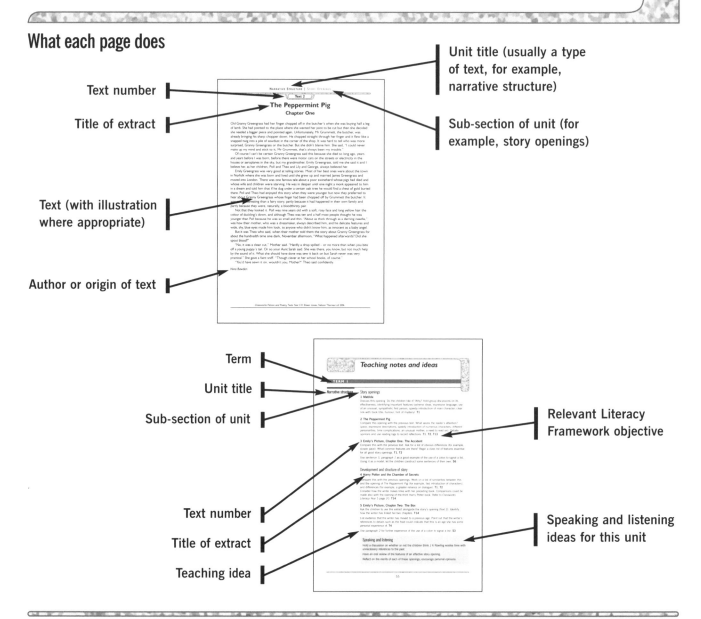

Text number

Title of extract

Text (with illustration where appropriate)

Author or origin of text

Unit title (usually a type of text, for example, narrative structure)

Sub-section of unit (for example, story openings)

Term

Unit title

Sub-section of unit

Text number

Title of extract

Teaching idea

Relevant Literacy Framework objective

Speaking and listening ideas for this unit

Matilda

It's a funny thing about mothers and fathers. Even when their own child is the most disgusting little blister you could ever imagine, they still think that he or she is wonderful.

Some parents go further. They become so blinded by adoration they manage to convince themselves their child has qualities of genius.

Well, there is nothing very wrong with all this. It's the way of the world. It is only when the parents begin telling us about the brilliance of their own revolting off-spring, that we start shouting, "Bring us a basin! We're going to be sick!"

School teachers suffer a good deal from having to listen to this sort of twaddle from proud parents, but they usually get their own back when the time comes to write the end-of-term reports. If I were a teacher I would cook up some real scorchers for the children of doting parents. "Your son Maximilian," I would write, "is a total wash-out. I hope you have a family business you can push him into when he leaves school because he sure as heck won't get a job anywhere else." Or if I were feeling lyrical that day, I might write, "It is a curious truth that grasshoppers have their hearing-organs in the sides of the abdomen. Your daughter Vanessa, judging by what she's learnt this term, has no hearing-organs at all."

I might even delve deeper into natural history and say, "The periodical cicada spends six years as a grub underground, and no more than six days as a free creature of sunlight and air. Your son Wilfred has spent six years as a grub in this school and we are still waiting for him to emerge from the chrysalis." A particularly poisonous little girl might sting me into saying, "Fiona has the same glacial beauty as an iceberg, but unlike the iceberg she has absolutely nothing below the surface." I think I might enjoy writing end-of-term reports for the stinkers in my class. But enough of that. We have to get on.

Occasionally one comes across parents who take the opposite line, who show no interest at all in their children, and these of course are far worse than the doting ones. Mr and Mrs Wormwood were two such parents. They had a son called Michael and a daughter called Matilda, and the parents looked upon Matilda in particular as nothing more than a scab. A scab is something you have to put up with until the time comes when you can pick it off and flick it away. Mr and Mrs Wormwood looked forward enormously to the time when they could pick their little daughter off and flick her away, preferably into the next county or even further than that.

It is bad enough when parents treat ordinary children as though they were scabs and bunions, but it becomes somehow a lot worse when the child in question is *extra*-ordinary, and by that I mean sensitive and brilliant.

Roald Dahl

Text 2

The Peppermint Pig
Chapter One

Old Granny Greengrass had her finger chopped off in the butcher's when she was buying half a leg of lamb. She had pointed to the place where she wanted her joint to be cut but then she decided she needed a bigger piece and pointed again. Unfortunately, Mr Grummett, the butcher, was already bringing his sharp chopper down. He chopped straight through her finger and it flew like a snapped twig into a pile of sawdust in the corner of the shop. It was hard to tell who was more surprised, Granny Greengrass or the butcher. But she didn't blame him. She said, "I could never make up my mind and stick to it, Mr Grummett, that's always been my trouble."

Of course I can't be certain Granny Greengrass said this because she died so long ago, years and years before I was born, before there were motor cars on the streets or electricity in the houses or aeroplanes in the sky, but my grandmother, Emily Greengrass, told me she said it and I believe her, as her children, Poll and Theo and Lily and George, always believed her.

Emily Greengrass was very good at telling stories. Most of her best ones were about the town in Norfolk where she was born and lived until she grew up and married James Greengrass and moved into London. There was one famous tale about a poor swineherd whose pigs had died and whose wife and children were starving. He was in despair until one night a monk appeared to him in a dream and told him that if he dug under a certain oak tree he would find a chest of gold buried there. Poll and Theo had enjoyed this story when they were younger but now they preferred to hear about Granny Greengrass whose finger had been chopped off by Grummett the butcher. It was more interesting than a fairy story, partly because it had happened in their own family and partly because they were, naturally, a bloodthirsty pair.

Not that they looked it. Poll was nine years old with a soft, rosy face and long yellow hair the colour of duckling's down, and although Theo was ten and a half most people thought he was younger than Poll because he was so small and thin. "About as thick through as a darning needle," was how their mother, who was a dressmaker, always described him, and his delicate features and wide, shy, blue eyes made him look, to anyone who didn't know him, as innocent as a baby angel.

But it was Theo who said, when their mother told them the story about Granny Greengrass for about the hundredth time one dark, November afternoon, "What happened afterwards? Did she spout blood?"

"No, it was a clean cut," Mother said. "Hardly a drop spilled – or no more than when you bite off a young puppy's tail. Or so your Aunt Sarah said. She was there, you know, but not much help by the sound of it. What she should have done was sew it back on but Sarah never was very practical." She gave a faint sniff. "Though clever at her school books, of course."

"You'd have sewn it on, wouldn't you, Mother?" Theo said confidently.

Nina Bawden

Text 3

Emily's Picture
Chapter One: The Accident

It all began with the weather. It had been unusually hot for England and everyone was struggling to keep cool. Temperatures had been in the 90s all week, with the usual consequences: weather forecasters warned of sunburn; ice cream sales were soaring; parks and swimming pools were full; and the wealthiest people were buying air-conditioning units.

Emily, however, was not wealthy. She lived in a small flat near the centre of town. Her daughter had helped her find and move into the flat, and everyone had said what a sensible move it was. Emily knew they were right – the old house was far too big for one person – but she did not like the flat. It felt claustrophobic, a tiny doll's house, stuck up in the air, with a window box for a garden. How she missed her old home!

She may have had to give up a lot of her furniture, but she had refused to be parted from any of her photographs: her memories were everything to Emily. The result was that photograph frames now jostled for space on the few surfaces she had; the picture of her as a child with her family was in a particularly risky place. It was positioned on a ledge just inside the sitting-room window.

Today the flat felt stifling. Every window was open; and Emily had switched her fan on, in a bid to stay cool. That was what did it – the fan. When the fan's current whipped back the curtain, the hem gave the photograph frame a passing brush. It was enough to make the frame lose its balance, and crash to the floor.

Clearing-up was a big job for Emily. The glass had shattered, and she was not sure when she would be able to buy another frame. In the meantime she must keep the picture safe. It was as she handled the photograph that some of the old questions and thoughts began to crowd into her mind. The mystery was still there. What had really happened in that strange summer of 1928?

Classworks Fiction and Poetry Texts Year 5 © Eileen Jones, Nelson Thornes Ltd 2004

Harry Potter and the Chamber of Secrets
Chapter One: The Worst Birthday

Not for the first time, an argument had broken out over breakfast at number four, Privet Drive. Mr Vernon Dursley had been woken in the early hours of the morning by a loud, hooting noise from his nephew Harry's room.

"Third time this week!" he roared across the table. "If you can't control that owl, it'll have to go!"

Harry tried, yet again, to explain.

"She's *bored*," he said. "She's used to flying around outside. If I could just let her out at night…"

"Do I look stupid?" snarled Uncle Vernon, a bit of fried egg dangling from his bushy moustache. "I know what'll happen if that owl's let out."

He exchanged dark looks with his wife, Petunia.

Harry tried to argue back but his words were drowned by a long, loud belch from the Dursleys' son, Dudley.

"I want more bacon."

"There's more in the frying pan, sweetums," said Aunt Petunia, turning misty eyes on her massive son. "We must feed you up while we've got the chance… I don't like the sound of that school food…"

"Nonsense, Petunia, I never went hungry when I was at Smeltings," said Uncle Vernon heartily. "Dudley gets enough, don't you, son?"

Dudley, who was so large his bottom drooped over either side of the kitchen chair, grinned and turned to Harry.

"Pass the frying pan."

"You've forgotten the magic word," said Harry irritably.

The effect of this simple sentence on the rest of the family was incredible: Dudley gasped and fell off his chair with a crash that shook the whole kitchen; Mrs Dursley gave a small scream and clapped her hands to her mouth; Mr Dursley jumped to his feet, veins throbbing in his temples.

"I meant 'please'!" said Harry quickly, "I didn't mean – "

"WHAT HAVE I TOLD YOU," thundered his uncle, spraying spit over the table, "ABOUT SAYING THE M WORD IN OUR HOUSE?"

"But I – "

"HOW DARE YOU THREATEN DUDLEY!" roared Uncle Vernon, pounding the table with his fist.

"I just – "

"I WARNED YOU! I WILL NOT TOLERATE MENTION OF YOUR ABNORMALITY UNDER THIS ROOF!"

Harry stared from his purple-faced uncle to his pale aunt, who was trying to heave Dudley to his feet.

"All right," said Harry, *"all right…"*

Uncle Vernon sat back down, breathing like a winded rhinoceros and watching Harry closely out of the corners of his small, sharp eyes.

Ever since Harry had come home for the summer holidays, Uncle Vernon had been treating him like a bomb that might go off at any moment, because Harry *wasn't* a normal boy. As a matter of fact, he was as not normal as it is possible to be.

Harry Potter was a wizard – a wizard fresh from his first year at Hogwarts School of Witchcraft and Wizardry. And if the Dursleys were unhappy to have him back for the holidays, it was nothing to how Harry felt.

He missed Hogwarts so much that it was like having a constant stomach ache. He missed the castle, with its secret passageways and ghosts, his lessons (though perhaps not Snape, the potions master), the post arriving by owl, eating banquets in the Great Hall, sleeping in his four-poster bed in the tower dormitory, visiting the gamekeeper, Hagrid, in his cabin in the grounds next to the forbidden forest and, especially Quidditch, the most popular sport in the wizarding world (six tall goal-posts, four flying balls and fourteen players on broomsticks).

All Harry's spellbooks, his wand, robes, cauldron and top-of-the-range Nimbus Two Thousand broomstick had been locked in a cupboard under the stairs by Uncle Vernon the instant Harry had come home. What did the Dursleys care if Harry lost his place on the house Quidditch team because he hadn't practised all summer? What was it to the Dursleys if Harry went back to school without any of his homework done? The Dursleys were what wizards called Muggles (not a drop of magical blood in their veins)…

J K Rowling

Text 5

Emily's Picture
Chapter Two: The Box

They were busy all week. Best muslin dresses had to be washed, starched and ironed; hair had to be crimped and curled; the house had to be made as presentable as possible; and there was the food to prepare. A feast was required.

Mother thought of everything: delicious soda bread; batches of griddle cakes; a huge joint of ham; a succulent piece of sirloin; boiled plum puddings; fruity parkin; and on and on. She was meeting strangers, and she was determined to be prepared. The wealthy relations from America would not find this house wanting.

Emily watched the flurry around her, as Mother and Cook grew busier and crosser every day.

"Out of the way, Emily," said Hannah. "Surely you can see that Madam and I are busy in the kitchen. You must wait to eat."

"Occupy yourself with your books, Emily," grumbled Mother. "It's too hot for me to be bothered by you."

It was hot – unpleasantly, stiflingly hot. Emily was listless and bored; she had no company; she was tired of her books; she needed novelty; and no one was remembering to check on her. That was how she came to make her discovery.

Emily took herself off to the garden. Looking for shade and relief from the heat, she went into the summerhouse. Rummaging in a disused cupboard, she made a find: a box, a box which at least held the possibility of novelty for her. The box did not look particularly special, but its contents kept Emily occupied: a number of pictures, some of them brown and discoloured; a large, dusty contraption which Emily half recognised as a camera; a small book; a pho…

"However did you find those?"

Her mother's voice was quiet; she looked white and shaken. Emily sensed that she had done something seriously wrong. She was yanked away, the contents were replaced, and the box was hastily returned to the cupboard.

"I do not want to hear mention of this. Do you understand?"

Charlie and the Chocolate Factory
Scene 3

Bucket home, several days later. GRANDPARENTS, MR *and* MRS BUCKET, *as before.*

MR BUCKET: You know, it sure would have been nice if Charlie had won that fifth Golden Ticket.

MRS BUCKET: You mean with that 10p we gave him for his birthday present yesterday?

MR BUCKET: Yes, the one we gave him to buy the one piece of candy he gets every year.

GRANDMA GEORGINA: And just think how long it took you two to save that 10p.

GRANDPA GEORGE: Yes, now that really was a shame.

GRANDMA JOSEPHINE: But think of how Charlie enjoyed the candy. He just loves Willy Wonka chocolate.

MRS BUCKET: He didn't really *act* that disappointed.

MR BUCKET: No, he didn't –

GRANDPA JOE: Well, he might not have acted disappointed, but that's because he's a fine boy and wouldn't want any of us to feel sorry for him. Why – what boy wouldn't be disappointed? I sure wish he'd won. I'd do anything for that boy. Why, I'd even –

CHARLIE: *[Running in excitedly]*: Mum! Dad! Grandpa Joe! Grandfolks! You'll never believe it! You'll never believe what happened!

MRS BUCKET: Good gracious, Charlie – what happened?

CHARLIE: Well… I was walking home… and the wind was so cold… and the snow was blowing so hard… and I couldn't see where I was going… and I was looking down to protect my face… and… and –

MR BUCKET *[Excitedly]*: Go on, Charlie… go on, Charlie… what is it?

CHARLIE: And there it was… just lying there in the snow… kind of buried… and I looked around… and no one seemed to look as if they had lost anything… and… and… and so I picked it up and wiped it off… and I couldn't believe my eyes –

ALL *[Except CHARLIE]* *[Shouting and screaming]*: You found the Golden Ticket! Charlie found the Golden Ticket! Hurray! Hurray! He did it! He did it!

CHARLIE: No… no… I… I found a 50p piece. *[Everybody looks let down and sad]* But, but, but… then I thought it wouldn't hurt if I bought a Wonka Whipple-Scrumptious Fudgemallow Delight since it was… my 50 pence… and I was just *sooo* hungry for one.

ALL *[Getting excited again]*: Yes… yes… go on… go on.

CHARLIE: Well… I took the wrapper off slowly… and –

ALL *[shouting and screaming]*: YOU FOUND THE GOLDEN TICKET! Charlie found the Golden Ticket! Hurray! Hurray! He did it! He did it!

CHARLIE: No… no… no… I ate the candy. There wasn't any Golden Ticket. *[Everybody groans and sighs, acting very sad again]* But then… I still had 45 pence left and… well… you know how I love chocolate –

MRS BUCKET: Oh Charlie, you're not sick are you? You didn't spend all of the money on –

CHARLIE: Well no, as a matter of fact… I bought another Whipple-Scrumptious Fudgemallow Delight… and… and… and I FOUND THE FIFTH GOLDEN TICKET!!!

ALL: You *what?*

CHARLIE: I did! I did! I really did! I found the fifth Golden Ticket!!

ALL *[Everyone yelling and dancing around]*: Hurray! Hurray! Hurray! *Yippppppeeeeeeeeeee!* It's off to the chocolate factory!!!

END OF SCENE 3

Roald Dahl, adapted by Richard George

Classworks Fiction and Poetry Texts Year 5 © Eileen Jones, Nelson Thornes Ltd 2004

Charlie and the Chocolate Factory
Scene 4

In front of the Chocolate Factory. CHARLIE *and* GRANDPA JOE *enter together as scene opens.*

CHARLIE: Boy, Grandpa Joe, I sure am glad that Dad let you take me today.

GRANDPA JOE: Well, Charlie, I guess he just feels that we understand each other.

CHARLIE: Plus, you seem to know all about Willy Wonka and what's happened to him.

GRANDPA JOE: Well, he's been an important man in this town for a good long time. A lot of people said some unkind things about him after he closed down the factory, but I always felt that he had his reasons. Actually I'm quite excited about this "Golden Ticket" thing. It's a good excuse to see what *is* going on in that factory and how he's running it.

CHARLIE: Speaking of the Golden Ticket, Grandpa Joe, could I read it one more time? I know it sounds silly, but the whole thing seems so magical.

GRANDPA JOE *[Searching his pockets]:* Sure, Charlie… let me see if I can find it… ah, here it is.

[He pulls out a small ticket]

CHARLIE: Let's see now… it says, "Greetings to you, the lucky finder of this Golden Ticket, from Mr Willy Wonka! I shake you warmly by the hand! Tremendous things are in store for you! Many wonderful surprises await you! For now, I do invite you to come to my factory and be my guest for one whole day – you and all others who are lucky enough to find my Golden Tickets. I, Willy Wonka, will conduct you around the factory myself, showing you everything there is to see, and afterwards, when it is time to leave, you will be escorted home by a procession of large trucks. These trucks, I can promise you, will be loaded with enough delicious eatables to last you and your entire household for many years. If, at any time thereafter, you should run out of supplies, you only have to come back to the factory and show this Golden Ticket, and I shall be happy to refill your cupboard with whatever you want. In this way, you will be able to keep yourself supplied with tasty morsels for the rest of your life. But this is by no means the most exciting thing that will happen on the day of your visit. I am preparing other surprises that are even more marvellous and more fantastic for you and for all my beloved Golden Ticket holders – mystic and marvellous surprises that will entrance, delight, intrigue, astonish and perplex you beyond measure. In your wildest dreams you could not imagine that such things could happen to you! Just wait and see!

And now, here are your instructions: the day I have chosen for this visit is the first day in the month of February. On this day, and on no other, you must come to the factory gates at ten o'clock sharp in the morning. Don't be late! And you are allowed to bring either one or two members of your own family to look after you and to ensure that you don't get into mischief. One more thing – be certain to have this ticket with you, otherwise you will not be admitted. Signed, Willy Wonka."

GRANDPA JOE: And today is the first of February, and say, Charlie – look we're here already… and I guess everyone else is arriving together.

[AUGUSTUS GLOOP, VIOLET BEAUREGARDE, VERUCA SALT, MIKE TEAVEE, MRS GLOOP, MR and MRS TEAVEE, MR and MRS SALT, MRS BEAUREGARDE enter. WILLY WONKA enters from opposite side]

MRS GLOOP: There he is! That's him! It's Willy Wonka!

Roald Dahl, adapted by Richard George

Charlie and the Chocolate Factory
Scene 4 (continued)

WILLY WONKA: Welcome! Welcome! Welcome! Hello, everyone! Let's see now. I wonder if I can recognize all of you by the pictures in the newspaper. Let's see. *[Pause]* You're Augustus Gloop.

AUGUSTUS GLOOP: Uhhhhh… y-e-a-hhhhhh and this is… uhh… my mother.

WILLY WONKA: Delighted to meet you both! Delighted! Delighted! *[Turns to VIOLET]* You're Violet Beauregarde.

VIOLET BEAUREGARDE: So what if I am – let's just get on with the whole thing, huh?

WILLY WONKA: And you must be Mrs Beauregarde. Very happy to meet you! Very happy! *[Turns to VERUCA]* I think you are… yes… you're Veruca Salt. And you must be Mr and Mrs Salt.

VERUCA SALT: Don't shake his hand, Daddy – it's probably all sticky and chocolatey from working in the factory. After all, he *does* only run a silly little factory. He's not important enough for you to bother shaking hands with, anyway!

WILLY WONKA: You're Mike Teavee. Enchanted to meet you! Yes… enchanted.

MIKE TEAVEE *[Blasting his guns]*: Come on! I'm missing all my favourite TV shows!

MR *and* MRS TEAVEE: And we're the Teavees. Pleased to meet you.

WILLY WONKA: Overjoyed! Overjoyed! *[Turns to CHARLIE]* And you must be the boy who just found the ticket yesterday. Congratulations! You're… Charlie Bucket – aren't you?

CHARLIE: Yes sir, thank you. And this, sir, is my Grandpa Joe.

GRANDPA JOE: Howdy, Mr Wonka. I'm real pleased to meet you!

WILLY WONKA: How do you do, Mr Grandpa Joe. How *do* you do! Well now, is that everybody? Hmm-mmmm… why… I guess it is! Good! Now will you please follow me! Our tour is about to begin! But *do* keep together! Please don't wander off by yourselves! I shouldn't like to lose any of you at this stage in the proceedings! Oh, dear me, no! Here we are! Through this big red door, please. That's right! It's nice and warm inside! I have to keep it warm inside the factory because of the workers! My workers are used to an extremely hot climate! They can't stand the cold! They'd perish if they went outdoors in this weather! Why, they'd freeze to death!

AUGUSTUS GLOOP: But… who… are these… uhh… workers?

WILLY WONKA: All in good time, my dear boy! Be patient! You shall see everything as we go along! *[All exit with WILLY WONKA remaining alone]* Are all of you inside? Good! Would you mind closing the door? Thank you!

[EXIT]

END OF SCENE 4

Roald Dahl, adapted by Richard George

Children at War
Production Notes

The play is suitable for a whole class production. There is a balance between acting and speaking roles, with scope for less confident children to work as part of a chorus or in miming groups.

SETTING

Scenery and props can be kept to a minimum. Use posters and labels to inform the audience when a change of setting occurs. Alternatively, narrators could announce where the action is taking place.

CAST

There are only a few named characters, but there is scope for as many speakers as preferred. In addition, there is the inclusion of a chorus, as well as narrators.

COSTUME

The play is set in 1939. History pictures will help when organising period dress. Similarly, make use of first-hand knowledge and advice from grandparents.

The chorus needs to dress plainly, preferably in black. Narrators could either match the chorus, or be dressed in period costume.

Alternatively, it could be effective to dress everyone very plainly in, perhaps, grey or black. Everyone would look the same, and attention would then be focused on the words and action of the play.

LIGHTING

Keep the lighting as subdued as possible. This will be in keeping with the austerity of the period. Too much light would imply wealth and modern material goods: the message must be the opposite.

Classworks Fiction and Poetry Texts Year 5 © Eileen Jones, Nelson Thornes Ltd 2004

Children at War
Playscript

Scene 1

Numerous children and adults are on stage. A cardboard nameplate gives the name of a railway station.

ADULT: Take care of yourself.

CHILD: Where's my mask?

CHILD: Where's my label?

ADULT: Look after our Elizabeth.

ADULT: Do as you're told.

CHILD: I want to stay home.

ADULT: Mind you don't mither.

CHILD: I want me blannie.

CHILD: Where's me snap?

CHILD: There's Billy!

ADULT: Oh, Dad, what will we do?

ADULT: Now you've upset her.

[A shrill whistle is blown by an adult, the teacher, who now comes to the centre of the stage.]

TEACHER: *[Speaking to audience]*
Look at the job I've got! Crying kids; moaning mothers; clinging Dads. What's the matter with them all?

They're going away on a holiday, out of noisy London, yet all they do is moan. *[Looking around at children, and shouting unpleasantly.]* Line up! Line up! Get on the train.

[General rushing around in circles as adults say goodbye, and children position themselves on an imaginary train.

The chorus is at the side of the stage. Some of their voices, low at first, sound out the rhythm of the steam train, while the others speak the words.]

CHORUS: They're off, they're off, they're on their way.
Nothing to stop them, nothing we say.
Wait for letters, wait for word;
Where are they going? Has anyone heard?
Miss city houses, miss city clack
Long for parents, want to be back.
They're off, they're off, they're on their way.
Nothing to stop them, nothing we say.

Classworks Fiction and Poetry Texts Year 5 © Eileen Jones, Nelson Thornes Ltd 2004

Mr Perkins and Darren
Chapter One: Trouble in Store

"In twenty years, it's the worst report I've ever read on a child: 'unmanageable; uncontrollable; intolerable; unbearable'. I won't terrify you with the rest of the words. You're going to have your work cut out, Perkins!"

The Headmaster's words could hardly have been worse. Cecil Perkins already had problems; the last thing he needed now was a new troublemaker in his class.

"Is he worse than Kindle?" he asked timidly. "Surely not as bad as Beaker?"

"Kindle! Beaker! Don't be ridiculous, man!" scoffed Mr Davies. "Those two are angels compared with the boy you're going to face on Monday. Let us down, and you know what will happen."

Mr Perkins quivered. The school's last Inspection had singled him out as being noticeably "different" for the following reasons:

- running an unruly classroom
- failing to extend all lessons to an appropriate length
- reading a magazine, instead of his Government Teaching Manual, during the stipulated reading session
- neglecting to apply a sufficient amount of red ink to exercise books.

In short, he was not to be trusted.

After that Inspection, Cecil Perkins had been watched closely – by visiting parent helpers; by classroom assistants; by other teachers; and by Governors. All had been required to submit regular reports to the Headmaster. The result was an official warning: either he gained "satisfactory" in the next Inspection, or he would be sacked.

Since then, Cecil Perkins had tried to fit in. He was improving his time-management; he kept an open Government Teaching Manual on his desk at all times; and he set up a system of bribery. Even Kindle and Beaker seemed to have swallowed the bait.

Now he was in a renewed state of panic. This "monster boy" was arriving on Monday; and so were the new Inspectors. He would have no time to talk this child into a bribery scheme. He realised that all he could do was fall back on his old ways, the ones that he had made up his mind to give up when he first started at this school. Reluctantly, he began to make his plans for Monday.

Classworks Fiction and Poetry Texts Year 5 © Eileen Jones, Nelson Thornes Ltd 2004

Dear Jane

Mel and Matt, ten-year-old twins, had little to worry about. Of course, they argued at home; wrestled with each other to reach the last biscuit; tried to avoid walking together on the way to school; actually caused bruises with the kicks they had been known to give each other when Dad was driving the car. Deep down though, Mel and Matt were friends. They needed each other.

You see, their mother had died when they were very young. Their family was small and close-knit – just Mel, Matt and Dad. The twins couldn't really remember their mother, but Dad had kept lots of photographs of her. In particular, he had given each of them a framed photograph to keep in their rooms; these photographs were precious.

The family managed well together. Dad was at work until six o'clock, but Mrs Santilal, their next-door neighbour, always gave them their tea, and Dad collected them later. Life was fine. The idea of change was not welcome.

It was in May that Dad re-married. Jane was her name. Of course, they had known about Jane for a while and, once or twice, had met her; but they had never thought Dad would marry her. Mrs Santilal was reassuring: said what a dear girl Jane was; how lucky the children were; and that they wouldn't need tea with a neighbour anymore. Dear Jane would be in the house now, waiting for them after school. Everyone seemed to expect the twins to feel excited, so they tried to be.

It was the first time that they were on their own with Jane, that Mel noticed differences. Her photograph of Mum: where was it? She had just got home from school, and it wasn't in its usual place. She tore into Matt's room to accuse him.

"I haven't been near your room," he protested.

Ben's Adventure
Chapter One: Clopton Grange

There had always been rumours, stories and fantasies, so much so, that it was now impossible to separate fact from fantasy. A child had died there, but the cause was disputed. There had been a fire, but the origin was not apparent. There were constant reports of unearthly sounds, but sources were never found. Dogs had shown terror, and had refused to pass the entrance. Figures from the past had been glimpsed, but always by a lone person. Imagination can easily run riot, so by now no one was sure what to believe.

The building's appearance matched its reputation. It was forceful, forbidding and frightening. A former property of the Crown, its upkeep had long been abandoned. The last owners were said to have departed suddenly, with word to no one; and for the last twenty years, the house had continued to fall into a deeper and deeper state of disrepair. The grounds were neglected, and looming trees left overgrown; daylight itself seemed to be barred entry.

Fortunately, there was no need for anyone to go near Clopton Grange. It stood on the highest point of a local walking area; to go past it, you had to make a deliberate detour. Local people gave the building a wide berth: they warned newcomers; parents guarded their children; the children spread rumours of ghosts; and the house stood alone. It would be a rare person who decided to venture near it.

Unfortunately, Ben was that rare person. He was a character attracted to mystery. He was curious, a seeker of answers. He formed his own opinions, and he dealt only with facts that he could prove. He was a local boy; and, of course, he had heard the rumours about the Grange, but they remained rumours. As the rumours grew, so did his interest: he must find out for himself.

However, although tempted to act alone, Ben was aware of the risks he might face: involving someone else would be wise. The question was "Who?"

Classworks Fiction and Poetry Texts Year 5 © Eileen Jones, Nelson Thornes Ltd 2004

Text 14

Problems

Miss Drummond drones on and on about these awful Maths problems. I can't understand Maths even if I concentrate until the steam comes out of my ears. Besides, I've got other things on my mind. I doodle on the back of my Maths book, write my name all sorts of fancy ways and surround each posh squiggly signature with elaborately entwined flowers. Then I write down Damian Chatham. He's this boy I like in our class. He's not my boyfriend. I wish! Damian's not the most good-looking boy and he's not the cleverest and he's not the best at sports – but he's funny and kind and I like him lots, though I'm too shy to let on to anyone, apart from my friend Lucy.

I don't know if Damian likes me or not. He said he liked my long hair once. And another time when I dropped the ball in Rounders and everyone groaned he said quietly, "Don't worry, Nicola." But that doesn't really mean anything. He's nice to everyone. He's nice to my friend Lucy. She's nuts about him too.

There's a little poke in my back. I turn around. Lucy passes me a note, keeping a wary eye on Miss Drummond. I have a peek under my desk.

Dear Nicola – Isn't this BORING!!! Do you have a clue what she's on about? Jenny and Mags and I are going down the Rec near my house after school. Want to come? Love Lucy. P.S. Damian and his mates often hang out there.

I read Lucy's note. I read it again. I read the last line over and over. I want to go down to the Rec with Lucy and Jenny and Mags – and maybe Damian! Soooo much. But I can't.

Dear Lucy – I write – Sorry, I can't make it after school. Don't you dare get off with Damian yourself! I haven't got a clue about the Maths problems either. Old Drummond could be talking some obscure Tuareg dialect for all I know –

Lucy never gets my note because Miss Drummond stops her long, involved Mathematical discourse and sees me scribbling. She asks me what I'm writing. I say, "Nothing, Miss Drummond." She sighs, beckons, and holds out her hand. I have to give her the note. She raises her eyebrows at the Old Drummond Tuareg bit. I hold my breath.

I'm terrified she'll give me a detention. I have to get back home for Mum. They know a bit about her at school, but they don't know how bad things are now. They still think Dad's around anyway. We can't tell them in case they have to report it.

It's almost a relief when Miss Drummond sets me extra Maths homework instead. I won't be able to do it, of course. I'll have to suck up to Clever Clogs Chrissie and bribe her with the Kit Kat from my packed lunch to see if she'll do the Maths problems for me.

"Sorry you got caught, Nicks," says Lucy, when the bell goes. "You coming to the Rec then?"

"I can't, Lucy"

"You *can*. Look, I tell you, I heard Damian chatting to Jack and Liam and Little Pete. They're planning to play footie there."

"You know I have to do the shopping for my Mum"

"Yeah, but you could do that after."

"I can't be late for her."

Lucy sighs. She knows about my Mum and me. I've sworn her to secrecy. But she doesn't understand.

"You've got to have some life of your *own*, Nicola," she says. Like it's a choice I can make.

Lucy's my best ever friend but sometimes I feel we're poles apart. She's at the North Pole spinning under the stars with Jenny and Mags and Jack and Liam and Little Pete and my Damian – and I'm down at the South Pole all by myself, unable to get hold of my own life.

I rush off without even saying goodbye properly. I don't want Lucy to see I've got tears in my eyes. I blink furiously and hurry down to Tesco's and buy all the food and stuff.

Jacqueline Wilson

Text 15

Carrie's War

For eleven-year-old Carrie and her ten-year-old brother, it had been a long day. Carrie had to be so grown-up…

Carrie wanted to cry suddenly. If she had been Nick she would have cried, or at least put on a hurt face. Being Carrie she stared crossly out of the carriage window at the big mountain on the far side of the valley. It was brown and purple on the top and green lower down; streaked with silver trickles of water and dotted with sheep.

Sheep and mountains. "Oh, it'll be such fun," their mother had said when she kissed them good-bye at the station. "Living in the country instead of the stuffy old city. You'll love it, you see if you don't!" As if Hitler had arranged this old war for their benefit, just so that Carrie and Nick could be sent away in a train with gas masks slung over their shoulders and their names on cards around their necks. Labelled like parcels – Caroline Wendy Willow and Nicholas Peter Willow – only with no address to be sent to. None of them, not even the teachers, knew where they were going. "That's part of the adventure," Carrie's mother had said, and not just to cheer them up: it was her nature to look on the bright side. If she found herself in Hell, Carrie thought now, she'd just say, "Well, at least we'll be *warm*."

Thinking of her mother, always making the best of things (or pretending to: when the train began to move she had stopped smiling) Carrie nearly did cry. There was a lump like a pill stuck in her throat. She swallowed hard and pulled faces.

The train was slowing. "Here we are," Miss Fazackerly said. "Collect your things, don't leave anything. Take care of Nick, Carrie."

Carrie scowled. She loved Nick, loved him so much sometimes that it gave her a pain, but she hated to be told to do something that she was going to do anyway. And she was bored with Nick at the moment. That dying-duck look as he struggled to get his case down from the rack! "Leave it to me, silly baby," she said, jumping up on the seat. Dust flew and he screwed up his face. "You're making me sneeze," he complained. "Don't *bounce*, Carrie."

They all seemed to have more luggage than when they had started. Suitcases that had once been quite light now felt as if they were weighed down with stones. And got heavier as they left the small station and straggled down a steep, cinder path. Carrie had Nick's case as well as her own and a carrier bag with a broken string handle. She tucked it under one arm, but it kept slipping backwards and her gas mask banged her knee as she walked.

"Someone help Caroline, please," Miss Fazackerly cried, rushing up and down the line of children like a sheep dog. Someone did – Carrie felt the carrier bag go from under her arm, then one suitcase.

Nina Bawden

Duck's Ditty

All along the backwater,
   Through the rushes tall,
Ducks are a-dabbling,
   Up tails all!

Duck's tails, drakes' tails,
   Yellow feet a-quiver,
Yellow bills all out of sight
   Busy in the river!

Slushy green undergrowth
   Where the roach swim,
Here we keep our larder
   Cool and full and dim!

Every one for what he likes!
   We like to be
Heads down, tails up,
   Dabbling free!

High in the blue above
   Swifts whirl and call –
We are down a-dabbling,
   Up tails all!

Kenneth Grahame

The Grasshopper and the Cricket

The poetry of earth is never dead:

When all the birds are faint with the hot sun,

And hide in cooling trees, a voice will run

From hedge to hedge about the new-mown mead:

This is the grasshopper's – he takes the lead

In summer luxury – he has never done

With his delights, for when tired out with fun,

He rests at ease beneath some pleasant weed.

The poetry of earth is ceasing never:

On a lone winter evening, when the frost

Has wrought a silence, from the stove there shrills,

The Cricket's song, in warmth increasing ever,

And seems to one in drowsiness half lost,

The grasshopper's among the grassy hills.

John Keats

Classworks Fiction and Poetry Texts Year 5 © Eileen Jones, Nelson Thornes Ltd 2004

Text 18

A Day in the Life of Danny the Cat

Danny wakes up
Eats
Finds a private place in the garden,
He returns
Plays with the plants
And sleeps.
Danny wakes up
Eats
Inspects the garden
Finds a cosy place
And sleeps.
Danny wakes up
Comes indoors
Inspects the carpet
Scratches himself
And sleeps.
Danny wakes up
Goes into the garden
Over the fence
Has a fight with Ginger
Makes a date with Sandy
Climbs on to next door's shed
And sleeps.
Danny wakes up
Comes indoors
Rubs up the chair leg
Rubs up a human leg
Sharpens his claws
On a human leg
Eats
And sleeps.

Danny wakes up
Eats
Watches a nature programme
Finds a private place in the garden,
Finds Sandy in next door's garden
Next door's dog finds Danny
Sandy runs north
Danny runs home
Eats and sleeps.
Danny wakes up
Checks for mice
Checks for birds
Checks for dogs
Checks for food
Finds a private place in the garden
Eats
And sleeps.
Danny has hobbies,
Being stroked
Car-watching
And smelling feet
He loves life,
Keeps fit
And keeps clean,
Every night he covers himself
In spit,
Then he eats
And sleeps.

Benjamin Zephaniah

Text 19

Days

Days fly by on holidays,

they escape like birds

released from cages.

What a shame you can't buy

tokens of time, save them up

and lengthen the good days,

or maybe you could tear out time

from days that drag, then pay it back

on holidays, wild days,

days you wish would last forever.

You could wear these days with pride,

fasten them like poppies to your coat,

or keep them in a tin, like sweets,

a confection of days

to be held on the tongue

and tasted, now and then.

Brian Moses

Seeing Red

I reach the lights:
I see red.
Prohibiting,
Halting,
Infuriating,
Red.
More delays,
Extra queuing,
Another hold-up,
Red.

Exasperated,
Impatient,
Ill-tempered,
I wait and fume.
I see red.

Text 21

The Raven and the Swan

The Raven was glossy black, with a sheen to be proud of. However, he did not like being black. He admired the beauty of the Swan, and he became jealous. Day by day, his envy grew. He wanted to be as white as the Swan, because he thought her great beauty came from her colour. If he became white, he would be equally beautiful.

Desperately, the Raven thought. At last he knew what to do: he made up his mind that the Swan had become so white and beautiful from constant washing and being in water. That was the answer! He must do the same.

So the Raven abandoned his way of living and moved to the lakes and rivers. However, his efforts were in vain: not only did water not change its colour, but also it did not give him his proper food. The foolish move cost him his life.

The Moral

We are not all the same, and must accept some differences. Some things we can change, but other characteristics can never be altered.

Adapted from *Aesop's Fables*

A Farmer and his Dogs

A Farmer, who normally treated his working animals well, became desperately short of food and money one year. In order to feed himself and his family, he had to use the animals that worked and provided for him. He began by killing the sheep, and using them for food. Still this was not enough; the family needed more food. The goat was next to feed the family. After that it was the cow, normally kept just to provide their milk; then the oxen that pulled the plough were killed and eaten.

The Farmer's dogs saw what was happening and held a meeting: could they also be in danger? They decided to flee, because they knew that if other necessary servants were being killed, the same fate would certainly befall them.

The Moral

In times of real need, people sometimes have to take decisions and act in a way that would usually be unacceptable to them.

Adapted from *Aesop's Fables*

Text 23

Little Red Riding Hood and the Wolf

As soon as Wolf began to feel

That he would like a decent meal,

He went and knocked on Grandma's door.

When Grandma opened it, she saw

The sharp white teeth, the horrid grin,

And Wolfie said, "May I come in?"

Poor Grandmamma was terrified,

"He's going to eat me up!" she cried.

And she was absolutely right.

He ate her up in one big bite.

But Grandmamma was small and tough,

And Wolfie wailed, "That's not enough!

I haven't yet begun to feel

That I have had a decent meal!"

He ran around the kitchen yelping,

"I've *got* to have another helping!"

Then added with a frightful leer,

"I'm therefore going to wait right here

Till Little Miss Red Riding Hood

Comes home from walking in the wood."

He quickly put on Grandma's clothes,

(Of course he hadn't eaten those.)

He dressed himself in coat and hat.

He put on shoes and after that

He even brushed and curled his hair,

Then sat himself in Grandma's chair.

In came the little girl in red.

She stopped. She stared. And then she said,

"What great big ears you have, Grandma"

"All the better to hear you with," the Wolf replied.

"What great big eyes you have, Grandma,"

said Little Red Riding Hood.

"All the better to see you with," the Wolf replied.

He sat there watching her and smiled.

He thought, I'm going to eat this child.

Compared with her old Grandmamma

She's going to taste like caviare.

Then Little Red Riding Hood said, *"But Grandma,*

what a lovely great big furry coat you have on."

"That's wrong!" cried Wolf, "Have you forgot

To tell me what BIG TEETH I've got?

Ah well, no matter what you say,

I'm going to eat you anyway."

The small girl smiles. One eyelid flickers.

She whips a pistol from her knickers.

She aims it at the creature's head

And *bang bang bang*, she shoots him dead.

A few weeks later, in the wood,

I came across Miss Riding Hood.

But what a change! No cloak of red,

No silly hood upon her head.

She said, "Hello, and do please note

My lovely furry WOLFSKIN COAT."

Roald Dahl

Text 24

The Blue Fish

Once there was a girl whose mother died. The villagers buried her body in the red earth beside the river. Everyday the girl drove the long-horned cattle across the plain, down to the river where they drank. Then she took them on to the hillside.

One day her father decided to get married again. But the woman he married hated the girl. She hated her so much that she gave her no food. Day by day the girl grew thinner. She grew so thin that her arms were like chicken bones, her ribs stuck out, her eyes lost their shine. She began to look like death itself. When she took the cattle on to the hillside she would scrabble about for roots and berries. Some days she found a bird's egg and crushed it raw into her mouth. And at night she lay in the corner of the hut, where the shadows gathered, and curled up tight with her knees against her chest – because that way it somehow lessened the hunger.

One morning, as the cattle drank, she stared into the depths of the river and cried. As her tears hit the water she saw a shape slowly moving through the water. It was a fish, a huge, blue fish. The fish spoke to her saying: "Why do you cry?" The girl began to tell this story, her story, and the fish said: "Come, step into my mouth." The girl stepped into the fish's mouth and it swam down, down, down through the cool water and spat her out at the bottom. She was in another place. There was a cloth with food upon it – bread, cheese, water, and meat. She ate until her stomach was tight – tight as a drum. Then she stepped back into the fish's mouth and they swam up, up through the cool water to the heat above. And, as they swam, the fish sang, "Oh child be brave, when I am dead, bury my bones in your mother's grave." She did not understand the words, but she did not forget them.

That evening she brought the cattle back across the plain. And for the first time for many months she slept. No longer curled up but peacefully stretched out – full at last. So it was, day after day, that the fish swam up to greet her and took her down to the other world where she was fed. Soon her eyes shone, her face filled out and she began to regain her strength.

One evening, when she returned hot and dusty from the plain, her stepmother waited in the doorway to the hut. The woman grabbed her by the arm and snarled "Who is feeding you?" The girl said nothing, she just closed her eyes. "Who is feeding you?" But the girl said nothing, she just lay down on the ground. "Who is feeding you?" But the girl said nothing, she just curled up tight. Then the woman took a burning brand from the fire and beat the girl – "Who is feeding you?" she snarled and with each word she beat the girl till in end the girl whimpered, "The blue fish... where the cattle drink." Then the stepmother stopped her beating and waited by the doorway – and the girl crawled into the shadows of the hut and curled up to sleep, her back bleeding from the beating.

When the father returned home, his new wife was waiting. "I'm poisoned," she wailed, clutching her stomach. "What can I do?" asked the husband. "I need fish – only blue fish will cure me," she exclaimed. "But where can I get blue fish at this time of night?" "Where the cattle feed," muttered his wife.

So the husband ran across the dark plain to where the cattle drank and he stared into the dark waters till he saw the vague shape of something moving upwards. As the fish broke the surface it opened its mouth to speak but the man's spear silenced it. As he ran back across the dark plain the fish was quite still in his arms. His wife took it greedily into the hut.

Traditional, adapted by Pie Corbett

Text 25

The Blue Fish (continued)

In the dawn light the girl crept out and down to the river. But the water was quite still – empty of any movement. That night she returned home and her stepmother was there waiting for her. "Here," she said, "I have some food for you – some soup." The girl took the bowl and stared into it. It was soup, fish soup, blue fish soup. She handed it back and went to curl up in the shadows. The woman sat and drank every bit of the soup, spitting bones on to the floor, wiping the grease from her lips.

In the morning the girl awoke. She could see her stepmother fast asleep. On the floor she could see white fragments of bone and she remembered the fish's song. She crept across the floor and quietly gathered up each bone. She made her way down to the rich red earth beside the river, where her mother was buried; there she dug the fish bones into the soil. That evening she returned to the river and where the bones had been buried she saw a bush – a beautiful, green bush with white flowers. Each flower was tinged with blue edges. She pressed the petals to her hot cheek, so cool, so cool. And beneath the bush there was a cloth with cheese, bread and fresh yams. She ate and made her way home.

So it was every day – more food and another white flower. Till one day the king's men came to the spot and saw her with a flower. One of them tried to pluck one for his girlfriend – but could not. Everyone then tried but the flowers could not be picked. So they returned to tell the king. That evening the girl came back to the bush. And there on the cloth was a pair of sandals. She strapped one onto her foot thinking – at last I will not have to run barefoot, treading on thorns and sharp stones. But just then she heard a noise – and coming towards her was the king, curious about this miraculous bush. The girl turned and ran, herding the cattle across the plain till she was just dust in the distance, leaving behind the king holding one sandal in his hand.

"In a month's time," declared the king, "bring all the girls to this place and we will see whose foot fits the sandal and who can pluck a flower from this bush." So it was that a month later all the villagers gathered and one by one the girls tried on the sandal. But it fitted no one. As the sun set and darkness fell the king ordered that bonfires be lit. Flames flickered far across the great plain by the rich red earth. "Who has yet to try the sandal?" asked the king – and someone remembered that the girl had come home late, hot, dusty and weary and lay asleep in the shadows, in the corner of her hut, where it was her place to be.

So a runner was sent to fetch the girl. Tired and only half awake, she stumbled out of sleep and ran across the dark plain towards the great fires that flared in the dark. And there beneath the great dark night, freckled with stars and shaped by the silver moon which was as curved as a horn, the girl strapped on her other sandal, plucked a white flower, cool to her cheek and tinged with blue, and became the king's wife.

Oh, there was such a feast. I wish that you had been there. You would have loved the singing and the dancing. You would have loved the storytelling – there, on the great, wide plain beneath the dark night, consumed by stars, with the curved moon riding high.

Traditional, adapted by Pie Corbett

Text 26

The Listeners

"Is there anybody there?" said the Traveller,
Knocking on the moonlit door;
And his horse in the silence champed the grasses
Of the forest's ferny floor;
And a bird flew up out of the turret,
Above the Traveller's head:
And he smote upon the door again a second time;
"Is there anybody there?" he said.
But no one descended to the Traveller;
No head from the leaf fringed sill
Leaned over and looked into his grey eyes,
Where he stood perplexed and still.
But only a host of phantom listeners
That dwelt in the lone house then
Stood listening in the quiet of the moonlight
To that voice from the world of men:
Stood thronging the faint moonbeams on the dark stair,
That goes down to the empty hall,
Hearkening in an air stirred and shaken
By the lonely Traveller's call.
And he felt in his heart their strangeness,
Their stillness answering his cry,
While his horse moved, cropping the dark turf,
'Neath the starred and leafy sky;
For he suddenly smote on the door, even
Louder, and lifted his head: –
"Tell them I came, and no one answered,
That I kept my word," he said.
Never the least stir made the listeners,
Though every word he spake
Fell echoing through the shadowiness of the still house
From the one man left awake:
Ay, they heard his foot upon the stirrup,
And the sound of iron on stone,
And how the silence surged softly backward,
When the plunging hoofs were gone.

Walter de la Mare

The Letter

A sweltering day,

Almost without cloud.

No racing about,

Just sun basking.

Then it came:

The letter.

An explosion,

A destructive force,

A venomous snake.

> My mother opened it.
> Her face was a page:
> "No" was written there.
> The word was clear.
> She made a call,
> Texted words which
> My father would read.
> The pen would write
> "No" on his face.

When she came out,

She told me the news.

I seemed quite calm.

Inside, I was broken,

A shattered egg-shell.

I was not going.

I'd let them down.

"Never mind," she said.

But I did.

Classworks Fiction and Poetry Texts Year 5 © Eileen Jones, Nelson Thornes Ltd 2004

Text 28

Hiawatha's Childhood

At the door on summer evenings
Sat the little Hiawatha;
Heard the whispering of the pine-trees,
Heard the lapping of the water,
Sounds of music, words of wonder;
"Minne-wawa!" said the pine-trees.
"Mudway-aushka!" said the water.
Saw the fire-fly, Wah-wah-taysee,
Flitting through the dusk of evening,
With the twinkle of its candle
Lighting up the brakes and bushes,
And he sang the song of children,
Sang the song Nokomis taught him:
"Wah-wah-taysee, little firefly,
Little, flitting, white-fire insect,
Little, dancing, white-fire creature,
Light me with your little candle,
Ere upon my bed I lay me,
Ere in sleep I close my eyelids!"

Henry Wadsworth Longfellow

Text 29

The School-time Rap

Dozing Sam at his desk one day,
Yawned at the Maths, wanted to play.
Drummed on his desk, gave it a tap,
Liked the noise, so started a rap.

Sam tapped on the top, then the floor.
He used his feet, and tapped some more.
Jumped from his seat, then gave a shout:
"Time's up, kids. We all need out!"

The rap caught on, the beat was hot.
It spread round the room, like a shot.
Teacher just gawped. Now what to do?
"Hey there, Miss, and that includes you!"

They formed a line, tapping their feet,
Clicked their fingers, feeling the beat.
Forget about Maths, this rap was fun.
Lessons were over, learning done.

Classes heard noise, they all joined in.
Pens tossed aside, books in the bin.
They danced on tables, rapped in hall.
School went crazy, had a rap ball.

Classworks Fiction and Poetry Texts Year 5 © Eileen Jones, Nelson Thornes Ltd 2004

My Pal

What a dog!

Too big.

Always oversized,

He dwarfed my human house.

How he ran!

Too fast,

Always outpacing,

He dragged me on my lead.

The welcome he gave!

Too friendly,

Always bouncing,

He floored me with a leap.

The tricks he knew!

Too clever,

Always thinking,

He stunned me with his skill.

The way I miss him!

Too much,

Always waiting,

I am lost without him.

Text 31

The Story of Persephone

Persephone was the beautiful daughter of Demeter. Her beauty was famous and it was envied by all, yet still she was loved by all for her gentle nature. Persephone had the sweetest of natures and she trusted everyone; but this trust was betrayed.

One day, as she strolled alone through the meadow, happily gathering flowers, she was seen by the evil Hades. Hades had long wanted Persephone to become his wife. Now he took his chance: he seized her and dragged her to the Underworld, the home of the dead. Later, when Demeter went to the meadow to find her daughter, there were only scattered flowers and signs of a desperate struggle. Frantically, Demeter began to search for her beloved daughter.

For years Demeter kept up her painful search. Without Persephone, all of Nature grieved: the skies wept; winds raced and howled; flowers withered; trees threw down their leaves; crops refused to grow. At last, in desperation, Demeter went to the all-powerful Zeus. She knelt before him and begged his assistance. He agreed to give help, but he made a condition.

True to his word, Zeus sent Hermes, his winged messenger, down to find Persephone. When Hermes flew down to the Underworld to demand the return of Persephone, Hades was told the condition. Poor Persephone. Caring as ever, she had always refused to touch the food belonging to the dead, except once, when she was tempted by a succulent, juicy pomegranate. She only had a little – just juice and some pips to quench her terrible thirst – but Zeus had made his condition: Hades must give Persephone up, only if she had not eaten any food of the dead.

Hades delighted in his triumph. He would not lose Persephone completely: for eternity, he would be allowed to hold Persephone in the Underworld for part of each year.

"Take heed, Persephone," he said "every year, when the air feels cooler, you must return to me for three months."

Text 32

How Fire Came to Earth

Zeus wanted to reward Prometheus and Epimetheus, the two Titans who had helped him in battle. So he gave them the job of making new creatures to scamper over the earth, and fill her woods and meadows with songs and joyful sounds once more.

"Here are the things you will need," he said, pointing to a row of barrels. "There's plenty for both of you." And he flew off back to Olympus.

Prometheus set about making some figures out of the first barrel, which was full of clay. He shaped two kinds of bodies, and rolled out long sausages of mud and pressed them against the bodies to make arms and legs. Then he made two round balls, and stuck them on the tops. He hummed as he worked, and his clever fingers shaped ears and eyes and hair and mouths until the figures looked just like tiny copies of Zeus and his wife. It took him a very long time, because he wanted his creations to be perfect.

In the time that Prometheus had made up his two sorts of figures, Epimetheus had made many. First he used up the barrels of spots, then he used all the stripes; he simply flung handfuls of bright feathers about, and as for the whiskers and claws he gave them out twenty at a time! By the time Prometheus had finished his men and women there was not a thing left to give them other than some thin skin, and a little fine hair.

Prometheus went straight to Zeus. "My creatures are cold!" he said. "You must give me some of your special fire to warm them up, or they will die!" But Zeus refused.

"Fire is only for gods. They will just have to manage," he said. "You shouldn't have been so slow in making them."

Now this annoyed Prometheus a lot. He had taken such care, and his creations had things inside that Epimetheus could never even have *thought* of. So he decided to steal Zeus's fire for them. He sneaked up to Olympus, carrying a hollow reed, and stole a glowing coal from Zeus's hearth. Then he flew down to earth.

"Keep this sacred fire of the gods burning always," he commanded his creatures. And they did. They looked deep into the flames and saw just what they should do. They built temples, and in each temple was a fire. And on the fires they placed offerings to the gods, and the smoke of them reached right up to Zeus's palace on Olympus.

Zeus liked the delicious smell. But when he looked down to earth and saw fires burning everywhere like little red stars, he was not happy at all. "Prometheus!" he bellowed. "I told you not to take that fire! I'll make you regret your stealing ways!" He swooped down on the back of a giant eagle and carried Prometheus away to the Caucasus Mountains, where he chained him to the highest peak. And Zeus sent the giant eagle to visit him every morning and tear enormous chunks out of his liver. Every night the liver magically regrew, so that poor Prometheus's punishment was never-ending.

But Zeus never took back the gift of fire from the earth, and we have it still to warm us on cold winter nights.

Traditional, retold by Lucy Coats

Text 33

Pandora's Box

Pandora was the most beautiful of women, but she was also the most inquisitive. She was forever curious, asking questions, wanting unnecessary answers, trying to find out about everything.

One day, when she was alone in a room, she spotted a large, heavy box that she had never seen before. The box was cumbersome for her to manage alone, so she called for her husband to come and help her move it. Epimetheus, her husband, was horrified when he saw what she had found. He became white and trembling.

"Move away! Move away!" he screamed. "You must never touch that!"

He dragged his wife out of the room. Then he explained that the box had belonged to his brother, Prometheus. When Prometheus had given it to him to look after, he had made Epimetheus swear never to disturb it or lift its lid. It had to be left closed until the end of time. Epimetheus begged his wife to forget all about the box. Very reluctantly, Pandora gave her husband her word.

However, Pandora remained as curious and inquisitive as ever. In spite of the warning her husband had given her, and the solemn promise she had made, she could not forget about the box. *What was in it?* She must find out.

The box was difficult to move, but this time she persisted. At last, she succeeded in lifting the lid. As she removed the lid, a swarm of buzzing insects flew at her, stinging and burning her as they made their escape. In panic, she slammed down the lid, but by then only one insect remained trapped in the box.

Pandora's curiosity had done a terrible thing. From then on, people would be stung by sickness, jealousy, envy, hatred and all the other evil, harmful sufferings that Prometheus had managed to trap inside the box. Only hope was still left in the box.

Classworks Fiction and Poetry Texts Year 5 © Eileen Jones, Nelson Thornes Ltd 2004

Text 34

Sir Galahad

Centuries past, Britain was suffering. It was a time of great famine, as crops failed to flourish, and plagues became rampant. Arthur was a good and popular king, but his people were growing impatient.

"Why can't King Arthur and his knights do something?" was the moan.

"It's fine for them in their fine court of Camelot," was a growing complaint.

"I thought his magician was supposed to be able to fix anything," came the sneer.

"Perhaps we should think of looking for a replacement," was the threat.

Arthur, with Merlin at his side, and supported by his noble knights, ruled Britain well. However, now there seemed no end to the country's misfortunes, and in vain, Merlin, the greatest magician ever, attempted to use his powers to find a cure. Nothing worked. Arthur knew that he must do something, and, deep down, he knew that he had only one hope.

Arthur was in despair, until a stranger arrived at Camelot. He was a young, handsome knight. He spoke and behaved confidently, and had the air of a nobleman. Striding, he moved towards the empty place at the Round Table. As he neared the empty chair, the letters of his name appeared: *SIR GALAHAD*. This must be a sign! The writing meant that he was the rightful owner of that chair. At last the Round Table of Knights – incomplete for so long – was complete.

The next day, Sir Galahad was led to the famed Rock. With no effort, he pulled Excalibur from the Rock; then he went on to lift the special shield that had proved impossible for all the other knights.

Now Arthur was certain: this was the man he had been waiting for! With Excalibur and this special shield, he was the knight who would lead the search for the Holy Grail. It was only the Grail that could end Britain's terrible suffering.

Text 35

The Legend of Romulus and Remus (1)

Amulius was king of northern Italy, but he lived in constant fear of attack. Therefore, when twin boys were born to his niece, he ordered that the boys be thrown into the River Tiber. The nursemaid took pity on them, and placed them as safely as she could in a wicker basket, before setting it to float in the river.

The basket floated downstream, before coming to rest among reeds. It was found by a she-wolf. The wolf looked after the newborn babies as if they were cubs. The babies thrived, well-fed and safe.

The years passed, until the boys were discovered one day by a shepherd. He and his wife cared for them, and taught them to be human beings: to eat, not scavenge; to walk on legs, not all fours; to talk, not grunt. However, as the boys grew to manhood, they became adventurous, straying from the shepherd's home.

News of the brothers spread. A local chieftain asked for them to be brought to him. As he listened to their story, understanding and recognition spread across his face: these were his grandchildren, the grandsons he had feared drowned years before!

The boys learned how their parents had been murdered by the king; and of how the throne belonged to their grandfather. Consequently, they helped their grandfather to overthrow the evil king and to reclaim his rightful throne.

However, the boys were dissatisfied. They were greedy for a city of their own, and they travelled to the spot where they had first been washed ashore and found by the wolf.

"This is where it must be," said Remus. "I must have my city here, the city of which I will be king."

"And I?" said Romulus. "Why should I not be king?"

The brothers proceeded to argue bitterly, each refusing to give in. They separated, one ascending the Palatine Hill, the other the Aventine Hill. A sign came: six vultures encircled Romulus. He claimed victory. However, he spoke too soon. A few moments later, twelve more vultures surrounded Remus.

"The sign is there," declared Remus. "I am worth two of you: I shall be king."

As the city was built, the brothers bickered ceaselessly. Eventually, in a furious rage, Romulus unsheathed his sword and killed Remus. Romulus called his city Rome.

Classworks Fiction and Poetry Texts Year 5 © Eileen Jones, Nelson Thornes Ltd 2004

Text 36

The Legend of Romulus and Remus (2)

Legend has it that Rome received its name from its founder, Romulus. He was one of a pair of twins, whose birth and upbringing were shrouded in mystery…

Leila, a royal handmaid, was washing clothes in the shallows of the river. She found herself becoming aware of a strange, mewing sound; the sound did not go away. Thinking it was a young animal in distress, she began to search among the reeds at the water's edge. Imagine her shock when she found herself looking down on the tiny forms of two babies. The tightly-wrapped infants had been meant to drown.

Leila, like everyone else, had heard rumours of the king ordering that two newborn babies be disposed of. She had thought the story to be mere idle gossip: now she knew better. In desperation, she tried to think what to do. If she took the children into the Palace, they would be doomed. Their only hope of survival was to be taken in by good people. With this hope, Leila placed the babies in her washing basket, said a prayer for their salvation, and put the basket into the River Tiber. She watched tearfully as it was carried away.

The babies were saved – but not by a person, by an animal. When the basket came to rest further downstream, it was discovered by a female wolf. Far from harming the babies, the she-wolf saved their lives. She cared for them, fed them, and reared them. Their lives among animals remained a secret until they were young men.

As they grew up, the young men grew restless, and were ready to leave their animal mother. They decided to build a new city, and chose as its site a beautiful place of hills. At first, they co-operated with each other, but gradually arguments broke out. Each of them wanted to be the supreme ruler, the king. The arguments progressed to blows, and finally Remus was killed by Romulus.

The winner of the fight owned his city: he called it Rome.

Classworks Fiction and Poetry Texts Year 5 © Eileen Jones, Nelson Thornes Ltd 2004

Changes

Eleni's birthday had been talked about for weeks. Now it was almost the day…

Eleni felt embarrassed already. It was her birthday on Tuesday, and everything was planned. Her mother had spent all weekend making cakes; her father had promised to finish work early; and even her younger brother had been persuaded to be on his best behaviour. The trouble was Nana.

Everyone else's grandmother seemed so young. Sophie's granny wore jeans and rode a bike. Lucy's grandma taught in their infant school, and was slim and elegant. Rupinder's gran collected him from school, dressed in eye-catching clothes. Nobody had a grandmother always dressed in shapeless, black clothes. Her mother had tried to explain.

"In Cyprus, when a woman's husband dies, she has to go into mourning for at least two years. To show everyone that she is still thinking about him, she must always wear black – and certainly not trousers or anything fashionable. For a widow to look too smart or glamorous would bring disgrace on her and her whole family. You must understand, Eleni."

Knowing all this still didn't make Eleni like it. Being Cypriot was wonderful. The other girls envied her long summer holidays in Lefkara, and Mrs Doyle had said that Eleni's mother had made their geography project more interesting because she had come to school to talk about growing up on a Mediterranean island. However, having Nana on show at her tenth birthday party was quite a different matter. She hatched a plan to keep Nana out of the way: she would show concern for Nana's health.

"My friends are very noisy, Nana, so it's best to stay in your room when they are here. The music will be terribly noisy, and I'd hate you to get a migraine."

Nana looked and sounded disappointed: "I was looking forward to a change, but I will keep out of your way."

What a relief! Eleni was sure she had done the right thing. After all, she was looking after her grandmother's interests, not just her own. Relieved, she set about completing her preparations for the party.

Text 38

Forbidden Clothes

"They are taking her away from us."

Mrs Khan articulated her words in a flat, monotone voice but, as she spoke, she leaned forward and stared intensely into the eyes of her volunteer English teacher, Margot Henderson.

Margot stared back, momentarily shocked out of her boredom. This was the first English sentence Mrs Khan had put together herself after nearly six weeks of lessons.

"What do you mean?" asked Margot.

Still leaning forward, Mrs Khan spoke again. She repeated the same sentence, hammering it out with staccato precision.

"They are taking her away from us."

"Who is taking who away from you?" asked Margot, looking round.

Then she met the large, dark eyes of the fifteen-year-old girl in the school photograph. It sat alone on the mantelpiece, testifying to the reverence and devotion accorded to an only child.

She wasn't beautiful. Her face had been left to fend for itself, framed only by a severe headscarf which swept her hair away out of sight. Her nose was too long and narrow, her cheekbones too angular, her mouth too broad. Yet there was something compelling about the way she looked almost defiantly into the camera, as if she was trying to say, "Yes, this is me. There's more to me than meets the eye."

"Nasreen." Mrs Khan whispered her daughter's name.

"Ah, yes! Nasreen!" repeated Margot, brightly. "How is she getting on at school?" Margot asked her question loudly and slowly as if the woman were deaf.

Mrs Khan opened her mouth and drew in her breath sharply as she struggled to find the words.

"She… she… not… fine. Fine…" She shrugged helplessly and slumped back into her seat, drawing her veil across her face.

Margot felt the irritation rising up in her. Mrs Khan was not her favourite pupil. She was a slow learner, and she resented the sense of dumb depression which seemed to envelop the woman, slowing down her movements and imprinting an expression of wooden despair on her face.

"Don't just say 'fine', Mrs Khan. Put it in a sentence," urged Margot with exaggerated patience. "Nasreen is fine."

"No!" exclaimed Mrs Khan sharply. "Nasreen is… no… fine…" she struggled desperately.

"You mean, Nasreen is *not* fine," corrected Margot.

"Nasreen is *not* fine," repeated Mrs Khan obediently.

"Is something wrong at school?" asked Margot. She glanced at her watch and noted with relief that their time was up.

Mrs Khan saw the movement. She stood up, twisting the ends of her veil in her fingers.

Jamila Gavin

Text 39

Rose

Rose is rocking her baby sister's pram when she overhears the conversation...

"Have you heard, Mrs Jenkins? Sweets are freed."

"It's about time, I suppose. Why should kiddies suffer? They didn't start the war. They need their treats."

Rose's mother only said that because face was important: she wanted the neighbours to think that she had money to spare. In fact, an end to sweet rationing would make little difference to her children.

When Rose overheard this conversation, she was "minding" as usual. She was the eldest, and she got the jobs. The list seemed endless: rocking the pram; stirring food; watching that no cat jumped on the baby's face; and constant errands to the shop.

"When I was eleven, I had to stay home and work. None of this gallivanting off to school every day," her mother would point out regularly. "Girls have no need for learning. You're very lucky to be staying on 'til you're fourteen."

However, Rose was unconcerned about anything today. When she heard her Mum's call to go and buy a packet of tea, she responded immediately. A trudge up the road? Take the pram so that the baby would fall asleep? Rose couldn't wait to get going.

Having bought the tea, Rose spent a long time inspecting the sweet jars. At last, she was ready.

"Two ounces of jelly babies; a quarter of humbugs; an ounce of rejects; four sticks of licorice; a quarter of humbugs; two ounces of..."

The shopkeeper interrupted: "Other customers are coming. That'll have to do you."

Never friendly, he seemed even grumpier than usual. Nevertheless, Rose was content to stop there – this time. From now on, Rose would be happy to shop daily.

"Right," said Mr Roberts. "Hurry up. Where's your money?"

Rose was surprised that he asked for money. Then she realised what had happened: if the news about free sweets was really new, Mr Roberts hadn't heard it yet.

"They're free, Mr Roberts. Haven't you heard? Sweets are free now."

"Free! Free! Is that what your mother has told you to say? And the tea next? Don't try your begging in this shop. Get out of here!"

Confused and crimson with shame, Rose fled the shop.

Classworks Fiction and Poetry Texts Year 5 © Eileen Jones, Nelson Thornes Ltd 2004

The Paradise Carpet

"One knot blue, two knots yellow, three knots red, four knots green…" The young boys chanted the pattern of the carpet they were weaving. Bony little fingers deftly drew the card down the thread; warp and weft… warp and weft… top to bottom, right to left… warp and weft and knot.

Behind a loom inside a dark mud hut, crouching like caged animals, sat a line of boys. With backs against a wall, their thin arms rose and fell as they drew the threads from top to bottom, right to left, warp and weft and knot. They could have been musicians plucking at strings, but these were carpet weavers whose harmonies were of the eye not the ear as, bit by bit, the glorious patterns and hues of a rich carpet emerged in the darkness. "One knot blue, two knots yellow, three knots red, four knots green…" The boys wove their thread, prompted and guided by old Rama, the only man among them, who had the pattern pinned to an upright in front of him.

"Ishwar, you're dreaming again!" bellowed a harsh voice. THWACK! The hand of the overseer struck a boy round the head.

The boy Ishwar, faltered and nearly fell over sideways, but Bharat, crouching next to him, braced his body and managed to keep his friend upright.

"Keep your mind on the job. There'll be no supper for any of you tonight until you've woven another ten inches," threatened the man. His great shape filled the doorway and blotted out their only source of light. Then he was gone. There was a low groan from the boys. Another ten inches before they would eat! That would take two hours or more, for this was the most complicated carpet they had ever woven – and the whole thing was to be completed within seven months – when an ordinary carpet took at least twelve.

A wealthy man had come along the rough track to the village in his white Mercedes. When he reached the brick house of Anoup, the carpet manufacturer, he got out like a raja, surrounded by shy jostling children and deferential elders, all of whom noted the gold rings embedded in his chunky fingers, and the chunky foreign watch just glinting beneath the cuffs of his smart suit.

"I want a carpet for my daughter's dowry," he declared. "She is to be married next December." (Everyone did an instant calculation. That was only seven months away.) "And this is the pattern I want you to weave."

Anoup took the piece of paper the rich man held out for him. He stared at it long and silently, then gloomily and apologetically shook his head. "Impossible," he said. "I need at least twelve months to do an average carpet – but this… this… and in SEVEN months, you say… No. Impossible."

The rich man pulled out a fat briefcase from the car.

Jamila Gavin

Text 41

The March of Time

Tick tock;

Tick tock.

Hear the beating of the clock.

Feel the time marching on:

Steady, measured;

Never pausing.

Seconds, minutes,

Hours and days;

Weeks and months,

Years, an age.

Time goes on;

It never falters.

Try to catch it!

Never will.

Tick tock;

Tick tock.

Hear the beating of the clock.

Text 42

A Teacher's Plea

Now, Class 5, I have some news:
The Inspectors are coming,
And this is a vital game
Your team can't afford to lose.

It's **You** they'll look at, not me.
So it's up to you to strive.
Conduct will be monitored;
No trick will escape scot free.

The Inspectors want it all:
Genres, Connectives, Phonemes;
Recounts, Reports, Instructions.
A single slip, you will fall.

Nothing stays beyond their sight:
My planning and my worksheets;
My targets and my outcomes.
Dear Class 5, please see **Me** right.

Classworks Fiction and Poetry Texts Year 5 © Eileen Jones, Nelson Thornes Ltd 2004

Text 43

Sounds of a New Day

The alarm clock shouts.

Stumbling footsteps,

Splashing taps,

The frenzy of the electric toothbrush.

Coffee-maker bubbling,

Toaster clicking,

Food crunches,

Liquid slurps.

A taxi horn beeps.

Doors slamming,

Voices mumbling,

Traffic rumbling.

Another day has begun.

Classworks Fiction and Poetry Texts Year 5 © Eileen Jones, Nelson Thornes Ltd 2004

Text 44

From **The Pied Piper of Hamelin**

Into the street the Piper stept,
   Smiling first a little smile,
As if he knew what magic slept
   In his quiet pipe the while;
Then, like a musical adept,
To blow the pipe his lips he wrinkled,
And green and blue his sharp-eyes twinkled,
Like a candle-flame where salt is sprinkled;
And ere three shrill notes the pipe uttered,
You heard as if an army muttered;
And the muttering grew to a grumbling;
And the grumbling grew to a mighty rumbling;
And out of the houses the rats came tumbling;
Great rats, small rats, lean rats, brawny rats,
Brown rats, black rats, grey rats, tawny rats,
Grave old plodders, gay young friskers,
   Fathers, mothers, uncles, cousins,
Cocking tails, and pricking whiskers,
   Families by tens and dozens;
Brothers, sisters, husbands, wives –
Followed the piper for their lives.
From street to street he piped, advancing,
And step for step they followed dancing.

Robert Browning

Text 45

From A Song About Myself

There was naughty boy,
    A naughty boy was he,
He would not stop at home,
    He could not quiet be –
        He took
        In his knapsack
        A Book
        Full of vowels,
        And a shirt
        With some towels –
        A slight cap
        For night cap –
        A hair brush,
        Comb ditto,
        New stockings,
        For old ones
        Would split O!
        This knapsack
        Tight at 'a back
        He riveted close
And followed his nose
    To the North,
    To the North,
And followed his nose
    To the North.

There was a naughty boy,
    And a naughty boy was he,
For nothing would he do
    But scribble poetry –
        He took
        An inkstand
        In his hand
        And a Pen
        Big as ten
        In the other,
        And away
        In a pother
        He ran
        To the mountains
        And fountains
        And ghostes
        And witches
        And ditches
        And wrote
        In his coat
        When the weather
        Was cool
        Fearing gout,
        And without
        When the weather
        Was warm –
        O the charm
        When we choose
To follow one's nose
    To the North,
    To the North,
To follow one's nose
    To the North!

John Keats

Text 46

The Jungle Book

Shere Khan, the mighty tiger, has succeeded in turning the Wolf Pack against the man-child, Mowgli. Bagheera has remained loyal…

"Now the business is in thy hands," said Bagheera to Mowgli. "We can do no more except fight."

Mowgli stood upright – the fire-pot in his hands. Then he stretched out his arms, and yawned in the face of the Council; but he was furious with rage and sorrow, for, wolf-like, the wolves had never told him how they hated him.

"Listen, you!" he cried. "There is no need for this dog's jabber. Ye have told me so often tonight that I am a man (and indeed I would have been a wolf with you to my life's end), that I feel your words are true. So I do not call ye my brothers any more, but *sag* [dogs], as a man should. What ye will do, and what ye will not do, is not yours to say. That matter is with *me*; and that we may see the matter more plainly, I, the man, have brought here a little of the Red Flower which ye, dogs, fear."

He flung the fire-pot on the ground, and some of the red coals lit a tuft of dried moss that flared up, as all the Council drew back in terror before the leaping flames.

Mowgli thrust his dead branch into the fire till the twigs lit and crackled, and whirled it above his head among the cowering wolves.

"Thou art the master," said Bagheera, in an undertone, "Save Akela from the death. He was ever thy friend."

Akela, the grim old wolf who had never asked for mercy in his life, gave one piteous look at Mowgli as the boy stood all naked, his long black hair tossing over his shoulders in the light of the blazing branch that made the shadows jump and quiver.

"Good!" said Mowgli, staring round slowly. "I see that ye are dogs. I go from you to my own people – if they be my own people. The jungle is shut to me, and I must forget your talk and your companionship; but I will be more merciful than ye are. Because I was all but your brother in blood, I promise that when I am a man among men I will not betray ye to men as ye have betrayed me." He kicked the fire with his foot, and the sparks flew up. "There shall be no war between any of us and the Pack. But here is a debt to pay before I go." He strode forward to where Shere Khan sat blinking stupidly at the flames, and caught him by the tuft on his chin. Bagheera followed in case of accidents. "Up, dog!" Mowgli cried. "Up, when a man speaks, or I will set that coat ablaze!"

Shere Khan's ears lay flat back on his head, and he shut his eyes, for the blazing branch was very near.

Rudyard Kipling

Text 47

Heidi

Chapter One: Up the Mountain

The pretty little Swiss town of Mayenfeld lies at the foot of a mountain range, whose grim rugged peaks tower high above the valley below. Behind the town a footpath winds gently up to the heights. The grass on the lower slopes is poor, but the air is fragrant with the scent of mountain flowers from the rich pasture land higher up.

One sunny June morning, a tall sturdy young woman was climbing up the path. She had a bundle in one hand and held a little girl about five years old by the other. The child's sunburnt cheeks were flushed, which was not surprising, for though the sun was hot she was wrapped up as though it was mid-winter. It was difficult to see what she was like for she was wearing two frocks, one on top of the other, and had a large red scarf wound round and round her as well. She looked like some shapeless bundle of clothing trudging uphill on a pair of hobnailed boots.

After climbing for about an hour, they came to the little village of Dörfli, half way up the mountain. This was the woman's old home, and people called to her from their houses all the way up the street. She did not say much in reply but went on her way without stopping until she reached the last house. There a voice from within hailed her. "Half a minute, Detie," it said, "I'll come with you, if you're going any farther."

Detie stood still, but the little girl slipped her hand free and sat down on the ground.

"Tired, Heidi?" Detie asked her.

"No, but I'm very hot," the child replied.

"We'll soon be there. Just keep going, and see what long strides you can take, and we'll arrive in another hour."

At that moment a plump, pleasant-faced woman came out of the house and joined them. The little girl got up and followed as the two grown-ups went ahead, gossiping hard about people who lived in Dörfli or round about.

"Where are you going with the child, Detie?" the village woman asked after a while. "I suppose she's the orphan your sister left?"

"That's right," Detie replied. "I'm taking her up to Uncle. She'll have to stay with him now."

"What, stay with Uncle Alp on the mountain? You must be crazy! How can you think of such a thing? But of course he'll soon send you about your business if you suggest that to him."

"Why should he? He's her grandfather and it's high time he did something for her. I've looked after her up to now, but I don't mind telling you, I'm not going to turn down a good job like the one I've been offered, because of her. Her grandfather must do his duty."

"If he were like other people that might be all right," retorted Barbie, "but you know what he is. What does he know about looking after a child, and such a young one too? She'll never stand the life up there."

Johanna Spyri, translated by Eileen Hall

William – The Fourth

William's mother has sent a photograph of William to his godmother; but now she is insisting on a letter…

"You'll have to write a letter to your godmother, dear," said Mrs Brown, as Mrs Adolphus Crane's birthday drew near.

"*Me?*" said William bitterly. "I should think I've done *enough* for her."

"No," said Mrs Brown firmly, "you *must* write a letter."

"I dunno what to say to her."

"Say whatever comes into your head."

"I dunno how to *spell* all the words that come into my head."

"I'll help you, dear."

Seeing no escape, William sat gloomily down at the table and was supplied with pen, ink and paper. He looked round disapprovingly.

"S'pose I wear out the nib?" he said sadly. Mrs Brown obligingly placed a box of nibs at his elbow. He sighed wearily. Life sometimes is hardly worth living.

After much patient thought he got as far as "Dear Godmother." He occupied the next ten minutes in seeing how far you could bend apart the two halves of a nib without breaking them. After breaking six, he wearied of the occupation and returned to his letter.

With deeply-furrowed brow and protruding tongue he continued his efforts. "Many happy returns of your birthday. I hopp you are verry well and so is mother and father and Ethel and Robbert." He gazed out of the window and chewed the rest of his penholder into splinters. Some he swallowed, then choked, and had to retire for a drink of water. Then he demanded a fresh pen. After about fifteen minutes he returned to his epistolary efforts.

"It is not raning to-day," he wrote, after much thought. Then, "It did not rane yesterday and we are hoppin' it will not rane tomorrow."

Having exhausted that topic, he scratched his head in despair, wrinkled up his brows, and chewed his penholder again.

"I have a hole in my stokking," was his next effort. Then, "I have had my phottograf took and send it for a birthday present. Some people think it funny but to me it seems alrite. I hopp you will like it. Your loving godsun, William."

Mrs Adolphus Crane was touched, both by letter and photograph.

"I must have been wrong," she said with penitence. "He looks so *good*. And there's something rather *sad* about his face."

She asked William to her birthday tea-party. To William this was the climax of a long chain of insults.

"But she wants you, darling," said Mrs Brown. "I expect she liked your photograph."

"I'm not going," said William testily, "if they're all going to be laughing at my photograph all the time. I'm jus' sick of people laughing at my photograph."

"Of course they won't, dear," said Mrs Brown. "It's a very nice photograph. You look a bit – depressed in it, that's all."

"Well, that's not *funny*," he said indignantly.

"Of course not, dear. You'll behave nicely, won't you?"

"I'll behave ordinary," he said coldly, "but I don't want to go. I don't want to go 'cause – 'cause – 'cause –" he sought silently for a reason that might appeal to a grown-up mind, then, with a brilliant inspiration, "'cause I don't want my best clothes to get all wore out."

"I don't think they will, dear," she said; "don't worry about that."

William dejectedly promised not to.

The afternoon of Mrs Adolphus Crane's birthday dawned bright and clear, and William, resigned and martyred, set off.

Richmal Crompton

Classworks Fiction and Poetry Texts Year 5 Eileen Jones, Nelson Thornes Ltd 2004

Text 49

The Secret Garden

Mary found the dining-room empty of people, but with food and drink left on the table. After drinking a glass of wine, Mary had become intensely drowsy…

Many things happened during the hours in which she slept so heavily, but she was not disturbed by the wails and the sound of things being carried in and out of the bungalow.

When she awakened she lay and stared at the wall. The house was perfectly still. She had never known it to be so silent before. She heard neither voices nor footsteps, and wondered if everybody had got well of the cholera and all the trouble was over. She wondered also who would take care of her now her Ayah was dead. There would be a new Ayah, and perhaps she would know some new stories. Mary had been rather tired of the old ones. She did not cry because her nurse had died. She was not an affectionate child and had never cared much for anyone. The noise and hurrying about and wailing over the cholera had frightened her, and she had been angry because no one seemed to remember that she was alive. Everybody was too panic-stricken to think of a little girl no one was fond of. When people had the cholera it seemed that they remembered nothing but themselves. But if everyone had got well again, surely someone would remember and come to look for her.

But no one came, and as she lay waiting the house seemed to grow more and more silent. She heard something rustling on the matting, and when she looked down she saw a little snake gliding along and watching her with eyes like jewels. She was not frightened, because he was a harmless little thing who would not hurt her, and he seemed in a hurry to get out of the room.

"How queer and quiet it is," she said. "It sounds as if there was no one in the bungalow but me and the snake."

Almost the next minute she heard footsteps in the compound, and then on the veranda. They were men's footsteps, and the men entered the bungalow, and talked in low voices. No one went to meet or speak to them, and they seemed to open doors and look into rooms.

"What desolation!" she heard one voice say. "That pretty, pretty woman! I suppose the child, too. I heard there was a child, though no one ever saw her."

Mary was standing in the middle of the nursery when they opened the door a few minutes later. She looked an ugly, cross little thing and was frowning because she was beginning to be hungry and feel disgracefully neglected.

The first man who came in was a large officer she had once seen talking to her father. He looked tired and troubled, but when he saw her he was so startled that he almost jumped back.

"Barney!" he cried out. "There is a child in here! A child alone! In a place like this! Mercy on us, who is she?"

"I am Mary Lennox," the little girl said, drawing herself up stiffly. She thought the man was very rude to call her father's bungalow "A place like this!" "I fell asleep when everyone had the cholera and I have only just wakened up. Why does nobody come?"

"It is the child no one ever saw!" exclaimed the man, turning to his companions. "She has actually been forgotten!"

"Why was I forgotten?" Mary said, stamping her foot. "Why does nobody come?"

The young man whose name was Barney looked at her very sadly. Mary even thought she saw him wink his eyes as if to wink tears away.

"Poor little kid!" he said. "There is nobody left to come."

It was in that strange and sudden way that Mary found out that she had neither father nor mother left; that they had died and been carried away in the night, and that the few native servants who had not died also had left the house as quickly as they could get out of it, none of them even remembering that there was a Missie Sahib. That was why the place was so quiet. It was true that there was no one in the bungalow but herself and the little rustling snake.

Frances Hodgson Burnett

Tom's Midnight Garden

Tom needs to find out more about his garden, but the doors are an obstacle…

The doors shut against Tom were a check upon his curiosity, until he saw a simple way out: he would get through the doorways that interested him by following at the heels of the gardener. He regularly visited the greenhouse, the heating-house, and used the south wall door.

Tom concentrated upon getting through the south wall door. That entry promised to be the easiest, because the gardener went through so often, with his tools. There must be a tool-shed somewhere through there.

The gardener usually went through so quickly and shut the door so smartly behind him, that there was not time for anyone else to slip through as well. However, he would be slower with a wheelbarrow, Tom judged; and he waited patiently for that opportunity. Yet even then the man somehow only made a long arm to open the door ahead of the wheelbarrow, wheeled it very swiftly through, caught the door-edge with the toe of his boot as he passed and slammed the door in Tom's face.

Tom glared at the door that once more was his barrier. Once more, without hope, he raised his hand to the latch and pressed it. As usual, he could not move it: his fingers seemed to have no substance. Then, in anger, he pressed with all imaginable might: he knitted his brows, and brought all his will to bear upon the latch, until he felt that something had to happen. It did: his fingers began to go through the latch, as though the latch, and not his fingers, now, were without substance. His fingers went through the ironwork of the latch altogether, and his hand fell back into place by his side.

Tom stared down at that ever-memorable right hand. He felt it tenderly with his left, to see if it were bruised or broken: it was quite unhurt – quite as before. Then he looked at the latch: it looked as real as any latch he had ever seen anywhere.

Then the idea came to Tom that the door might be no more solid than the latch, if he really tried it.

Deliberately he set his side against the door, shoulder, hip and heel, and pressed. At first, nothing gave, either of himself or the door. Yet he continued the pressure, with still greater force and greater determination; and gradually he became aware of a strange sensation, that at first he thought was a numbness all down his side – but no, it was not that.

"I'm going through," Tom gasped, and was seized with alarm and delight.

On the other side of the wall, the gardener had emptied his barrow-load of weeds and was sitting on the handle of his barrow, in front of a potting shed, eating his midday dinner. If he had been able to see Tom at all he would have seen a most curious sight: a very thin slice of boy, from shoulder to foot, coming through a perfectly solid wooden door. At first the body came through evenly from top to bottom; then, the upper part seemed to stop, and the bottom part came through in its entirety, legs first. Then one arm came through, then another. Finally, everything was through except the head.

The truth was that Tom was now a little lacking courage. The passing through the door of so much of his body had not been without enormous effort and peculiar, if indescribable, sensations. "I'm just resting a minute," said Tom's head, on the garden side of the door; yet he knew that he was really delaying because he was nervous.

Philippa Pearce

Teaching notes and ideas

Narrative structure

Story openings

1 Matilda
Discuss this opening. Do the children like it? Why? Hold group discussions on its effectiveness, identifying important features (extreme ideas; expressive language; use of an unusual sympathetic first person; speedy introduction of main character; clear link with book title; humour; hint of mystery). **T1**

2 The Peppermint Pig
Compare this opening with the previous text. What seizes the reader's attention? (pace; expressive descriptions; speedy introduction of numerous characters; different personalities; time complications; an unusual mother; a need to read on). Debate opinions and use reading logs to record reflections. **T1**, **T2**, **T13**

3 Emily's Picture, Chapter One: The Accident
Compare this with the previous text. Ask for a list of obvious differences (for example, slower pace). What common features are there? Begin a class list of features essential for all good story openings. **T1**, **T2**

Use sentence 3, paragraph 1 as a good example of the use of a colon to signal a list. Using it as a model, let the children construct some sentences of their own. **S6**

Development and structure of story

4 Harry Potter and the Chamber of Secrets
Compare this with the previous openings. Work on a list of similarities between this and the opening of *The Peppermint Pig* (for example, fast introduction of characters), and differences (for example, a greater reliance on dialogue). **T1**, **T2**

Consider how the writer makes links with her preceding book. Comparisons could be made also with the opening of the third Harry Potter book. Refer to *Classworks Literacy Year 5* page 20. **T14**

5 Emily's Picture, Chapter Two: The Box
Ask the children to use this extract alongside the story's opening (Text 3). Identify how the writer has linked her two chapters. **T14**

List evidence that the writer has moved to a previous age. Point out that the writer's references to details such as the food could indicate that this is an age she has some personal experience of. **T4**

Use paragraph 2 for further experience of the use of a colon to signal a list. **S3**

Speaking and listening
Hold a discussion on whether or not the children think J K Rowling wastes time with unnecessary references to the past.

Have an oral review of the features of an effective story opening.

Reflect on the merits of each of these openings; encourage personal opinions.

Plays

6–8 Charlie and the Chocolate Factory

Use the script for reading and acting. Make sure that the children are familiar with dramatic conventions. **T5**

9 Children at War: Production Notes

Consider the value of production notes. Ask the children to list and familiarise themselves with appropriate vocabulary. **T5**

Let the children create their own production notes for *Charlie and the Chocolate Factory*. **T18**

10 Children at War: Playscript

Read this, pointing out some of the conventions of scripting. **T5**

Identify strange vocabulary. Talk about the use of dialect words, and identify ones used here. Discuss probable meanings. (Blannie = blanket; mither = pester; snap = snack.) **S2**

Ask the children to add further stage directions. **T19**

Put the children into groups to write Scene 2 in this play. Ask for production notes; annotation; dramatic conventions. **T18**, **T19**

Hold performances of the scenes. **T20**

Speaking and listening

Encourage a constructive class discussion, in which the scripts and performances of Scene 2 of *Children at War* are evaluated. **T20**

Were there places where characters came to life because of a gesture? Emphasise the need for this to be included in a script.

Talk about opportunities for a class production (a school assembly?) and collect initial ideas.

Collaborate on preparations.

Aspects of narrative

Story beginnings and characters

11 Mr Perkins and Darren

Focus on the immediacy of this opening: an immediate problem; and a conversation that seems to have already begun. Use the conversation as a revision tool for the rules for the layout of dialogue. **S7**

Explain the difference between direct and reported speech. Model changing from one type to the other; highlight word and punctuation changes.

Ask the children to transform this conversation into reported speech. **S5**

Ask the children to list words and phrases which give information about the headmaster's and the teacher's different personalities. Consider the reader's response. **T3**

12 Dear Jane

Ask the children to identify which character they think is going to be the most important. Make sure that they recognise the relevance of the title. Ask the children to list references to Jane. How does the reader respond at this stage? **T3**

Let the children continue writing the conversation that has just started, using direct speech. **S7**

13 Ben's Adventure

Compare this story opening with others met in this unit (and you could also compare it with those in the unit on narrative structure, Texts 1–5). Ask the children to list some differences. Point out the emphasis on <u>where</u> the action takes place: a building is given greater detail than any character. Discuss the effectiveness of this and experiment with alternative openings. **T11**

14 Problems

Focus on the informal, 'chatty' style. Do the children notice this? Which words give this tone? How much does the reader learn about Nicola in this opening? What device is the author using? Compare this with the character presentation in *Dear Jane* (Text 12) and *Ben's Adventure* (Text 13). **T3**

Talk about the current popularity of Jacqueline Wilson. Have the children read any of her work? Consider making a reading journal entry about *Problems* or another of her books. **T10, T12**

Incorporate ICT into this Literacy work, giving the children access to computers for research. A website would provide information for research on the author and her books; at the time of writing, *www.channel4.com/learning/microsites/B/bookbox* is a very useful resource.

15 Carrie's War

Point out that many of Nina Bawden's books are now regarded as 'modern classics'. How does her work differ from Text 14? **T12**

Ask the children to investigate how the character of Carrie is presented. How is the reader given insight into Carrie's feelings? Ask for textual references. Consider the importance of Carrie's relationship with her brother. How does the author want the reader to respond to the character? **T3**

Ask the children to write the next chapter in *Carrie's War*, introducing a new character – perhaps the unnamed character at the end of this extract. (Discourage them from relying on television versions or a knowledge of the book.) They need to maintain consistency, remembering: when it is set; facts already given; the style of the author. **T15**

Speaking and listening

Discuss the different ways characters have been presented in this unit.

Which writing devices do the children find most effective?

Make use of some of the characters for role play: the class asks questions of a character. The person playing the character must respond in a way that fits in with the rest of the text.

Encourage the children to express their own opinions on a 'modern classic' such as *Carrie's War*. (Widen the discussion to include older 'classics'.)

Poetry

16 Duck's Ditty

Analyse the poem's style and structure: regular stanzas; regular rhyme pattern; its use of repetition; the punctuation used. **T6, T7**

Do the children like the poem? Which words and phrases do they find memorable?

17 The Grasshopper and the Cricket

Compare the content and style of this poem with the previous one. **T6**

Ask the children to 'plot' the rhyme pattern as you recite the poem. How does the second half of the poem differ from the first half? Does the changed pattern suit the changed season? **T7**, **T8**

Ask the children for their preferences from the two poems, and written justifications which refer to the texts. **T7**

Provide opportunities for research on Keats, and similar poems by him. Guide the children towards significant features in his style and content. **T6**

18 A Day in the Life of Danny the Cat

Analyse the poetic style, with its everyday tone. Is this typical of Zephaniah? Use, for example, *www.channel4.com/learning/microsites/B/bookbox* for initial research on the poet; decide on distinctive themes and characteristics of his work. **T6**, **T7**

Ask the children to search for a pattern in the poem's construction and language – for example, the repetition of 'Danny wakes up'. **T7**

Use this poem as a model for the children's own writing.

Compare the ways the three poets have treated the subject of animal life. **T6**

19 Days

Focus on the poem's imagery. Revise similes and metaphors. What examples are in the poem? Ask the children to turn Moses's similes into metaphors; and try to add metaphors of their own. **T17**

20 Seeing Red

Ask the children to identify words which reflect the poet's mood and feelings. Discuss how the poet decided on her word selection. **T16**

Do the children understand the double meaning of 'seeing red'? Collaborate on a list of other idioms involving word play – for example, 'blowing hot and cold'.

Let the children draft poems based on these other examples of word play. **T8**

Speaking and listening

Emphasise that poems are to be heard, not just read. Enjoy a recitation session.

Encourage the expression of opinions. 'Which poem did you enjoy? Why?'

Provide opportunities for the children to use a partner as a 'sounding board' for the selection of words or lines in their writing drafts. Poems can then be edited accordingly.

TERM 2

Traditional stories and fables

Fables

21 The Raven and the Swan

Explore the meaning of the fable. Ask children to retell the story orally. Consider the differences and similarities between oral and written storytelling.

Begin a class list of the features of a fable. **T1**

22 A Farmer and his Dogs

Collaborate in completing a list of features for fables. Consider alternative morals for this fable.

Ask the children to write their own fables, perhaps with you supplying the theme, animals or moral. **T1**, **T11**

Stories

23 Little Red Riding Hood and the Wolf

Ask the children to map the plot of the traditional story of *Little Red Riding Hood*; and then to map the plot of this one. Can they identify the key differences? Do they know any other versions of the story? **T2**

24–25 The Blue Fish

Explain that this is a traditional tale, with oral origins, from southern Africa. After reading, ask the children to make notes on the story outline in preparation for oral storytelling. **T3**, **T14**

Point out some differences between written and spoken language. **S6**

Speaking and listening

Hold an oral storytelling session, using the children's own fables, and perhaps involving a younger class.

Hold an oral storytelling session, the children using their notes on *The Blue Fish*.

Discuss *The Blue Fish*. Do the children recognise a link with *Cinderella*. Explain that the themes in *Cinderella* are common to folk tales across many cultures.

Poetry

Narrative poems

26 The Listeners

Define the term 'narrative poetry', and supply background information about the poet. Experiment with different readings of the poem, for instance: a single voice or group of voices for the Traveller's words; using background sounds to represent the noises mentioned; splitting the poem into sections, to be spoken by different groups of children; varying volume. **T4**

27 The Letter

Point out the simplicity of the storytelling format in this narrative poem. In contrast, there is effective use of figurative language; ask the children to identify examples. Clarify the distinction between words used literally and figuratively. **T4**, **T10**

28 Hiawatha's Childhood

Point out how much more lyrical this poem is than Text 27 and discuss how this is achieved. **T4**

Stress the focus on sound in the vocabulary, and ask the children to pick out onomatopoeic words. Work on finding and inventing alternatives. **W11**

This would be an enjoyable poem for the children both to perform and add another verse to. **T5**

Poetic variety

29 The School-time Rap

Ask the children to research the origins of this type of poetry. This should be fun to perform and would make a useful model for the children's own versions, perhaps working in groups. **T5**, **T6**, **T12**

30 My Pal

This is an elegy to a pet. Define the type of poetry, and its usual use. (An elegy is a poem or song written to lament a person's death.) Point out the regular pattern of the verses, but the absence of rhyme. Notice also how roles are sometimes reversed here, with the dog in charge of the person: He dragged me on my lead. **T6**

Ask the children to each choose a favourite poem from this unit, and to write comments, justifying their choices. **T7**

Speaking and listening

Hold a rap session. Let the children be an audience for one another's poems, evaluating the performances according to pre-defined criteria.

Discuss the children's choices and reasons, agreeing on poems to be included in your class anthology.

Myths and legends

Myths

31 The Story of Persephone

Ask the children to define a myth and to list the features they expect to find. Collaborate on creating a class list. Ask the children to identify features in this myth. **T1**

32 How Fire Came to Earth

Mark this myth against the checklist of features. **T1**

Ask the children to write their own myths, bearing in mind the important features noted (see above). **T11**

Point out the use of a storyteller character, and make clear the distinction between the storyteller and the author. Investigate how the main characters are treated. **T8**

33 Pandora's Box

Discuss the powerful visual images in the story. Do the children know the difference between literal and figurative language? Ask the children to explain the message behind the escape of the stinging insects. Why is it important that there is still hope left in the box? **T10**

Legends

34 Sir Galahad

Ask the children to define a legend and to list the features they expect to find. Collaborate on creating a class list. Ask the children to identify features in this legend. **T1**

35 The Legend of Romulus and Remus (1)

Ask the children to help you identify the key features of a legend using this text as an example. **T1**

36 The Legend of Romulus and Remus (2)

Discuss how and why changes may occur in stories over time. Ask the children to list the points of difference between the two legends of Romulus and Remus. **T2**

Let the children write a third version of the legend. (They could research this using the library or internet.) Decide on the target audience – perhaps Year 2/3 – and remind the children to make sentence structure and vocabulary appropriate for that age group. **S3**

Speaking and listening

Do some role-play activities, with children answering questions in character.

Discuss myths and legends the children know from film versions. What are the relative merits of print and film?

TERM 3

Narrative: empathy/ point of view

37 Changes
Investigate aspects of different cultural customs and traditions mentioned. **T1**

From which point of view is the story told? Which character does the reader feel most empathy with? Which words and actions evoke a response? Ask the children for textual references. **T1**, **T2**

Set the task of writing a new version of these same events, but from Nana's point of view. **T7**

38 Forbidden Clothes
Discuss which character the reader feels empathy with. Ask the children to support answers with textual references. **T2**

Ask the children to list points of cultural differences or conflict. **T1**

Focus on Mrs Khan's speech. Consider the errors she makes and how they can be corrected.

Give the children some sentences for correction: include errors such as double negatives, or non-agreement between verbs and subjects. **S1**

39 Rose
Ask the children to find the ways in which this story reflects different attitudes from those in the UK today. **T1**

Highlight the need to avoid non-standard words in order to have general comprehension. Which words do the children have difficulty understanding? Discuss why. **S1**

40 The Paradise Carpet
Consider the setting of the story; the traditions mentioned; the distinction between rich and poor. **T1**

Ask the children to quote words which reinforce the reader's sympathy for the boys. **T2**

Speaking and listening
Discuss Eleni's embarrassment in *Changes*. Do the children empathise with this? Have they had similar experiences?

Retell *Rose* from a different viewpoint.

Poetry

Modern choral and performance poetry

41 The March of Time
Focus on a steady beat for the poem. Perform with a mix of voices, experimenting with numbers of voices and volume.

Let the children plan group performances. **T4**

42 A Teacher's Plea
Discuss the content, structure, regularity and rhyme pattern of the poem. Point out that the early emphasis on 'you' is finally replaced by 'me'; the oral tone of the poem should reflect this. **T4**

43 Sounds of a New Day

A chorus could supply the sounds being mentioned. Experiment with different ideas for performance. **T4**

Plan group performances of the poem. **T4**

Use one of the poems as a model for the children's own writing. **T11**

Older poetry

44 *From* The Pied Piper of Hamelin

Increasing volume and speed are important as the noise of the rats grows. Let the children work in groups to rehearse and modify their performances. **T4**

45 *From* A Song About Myself

Ask the children to conduct some research on the poet. Does any language present difficulty? **T6**

Explain that this is an example of nonsense verse. Investigate how the poet has played with words, perhaps using this work as a model for the children's own nonsense verses. **T11**

Speaking and listening

Share the group performances.

Give opportunities for the children to try out their poems on others and edit them accordingly.

Narrative: author style

Older literature

46 The Jungle Book

Ask the children to research the author and date of this book. How is its age apparent? Identify examples of old-fashioned, formal language. **T6**

Make a comparison between this written version and film versions. **T6**

Consider the reading level of the extract. Focus on sentence structure and the difficulties for a younger, modern reader.

Ask the children to adapt a section for a younger audience. **S2**

47 Heidi

Provide background information and discuss the problems of translation. How will this affect language and style?

Use reading journals to record reactions to this story opening, as well as predictions for how the story will proceed. **T8**

Ask the children to write discursively about this story opening, commenting on its impact when compared with modern books they have read recently. **T10**

48 William – The Fourth

Discuss the time period of this story. Ask the children to identify clues in the text. Consider if the language makes the text inaccessible. (Martin Jarvis's tapes of shortened adaptations of some of these stories have been used on BBC Radio 4 in recent years.)

Do they find the main character appealing? (Compare with *Harry Potter*.)

Brainstorm ideas on what could happen next. Ask the children to complete the chapter, retaining the original author style. **T9**

Make reading journal entries, recording reactions to the text. **T8**

Ask the children to re-write William's letter, correcting his spelling mistakes. **W3**

Use some of the misspelt words – for example 'hoppin' – to revise spelling rules. **W5**

Ask the children to list any grammatical errors William makes in his letter or his speech. Use these as the basis of a lesson on the conventions of standard English. **S1**

49 The Secret Garden
Conduct some research on the author and date of this book. Discuss the story's setting. Let the children identify words, customs or traditions that indicate different cultures.

Ask the children to plan, write, proofread and edit a discursive piece of writing, commenting on the main character, Mary Lennox. **T10**

50 Tom's Midnight Garden
Discuss what happens in this extract and where the story could go next. Share ideas. Make reading journal entries, predicting what will happen. **T8**

Investigate the author's style: vocabulary; descriptions; types of sentences; punctuation. Ask the children to write the next chapter in this style. **T9**

Speaking and listening
Debate the merits of older literature. Discuss how and why it can still appeal to a modern reader.

Ask the children to talk about older books that they have enjoyed.